HOW TO REACH ANYONE WHO'S ANYONE

BY MICHAEL LEVINE

PRICE/STERN/SLOAN

Publishers, Inc., Los Angeles

1980

Dedicated to my wife Darlene, without whom this book, like most things in my life, would have been impossible.

You Are Someone!

Best,

INTRODUCTION

The biggest question regarding writing to notables is, "How can I make sure the notable receives my letter?" Well, the number one reason why mail is left unanswered is that it is addressed improperly and never reaches its intended destination. A letter addressed "Liza Minnelli, Hollywood, CA" will find its way only to a dead letter file at the post office. And so, this book . . . complete, correct addresses that will get your mail to the homes, offices, agents, studios or managers of the addressees.

Following are other commonly asked questions:

Q. Will the notable personally read the letter I send?

A. Some do and some don't. You must remember that most notables are busy, hard-working people. Some of the very popular celebrities receive as many as 50,000 pieces of mail each week. But there isn't anyone who doesn't at some point take time out to read at least a sampling of mail. Your letter, if properly addressed, has as good a chance as anyone's to be in that sample.

Q. Is there any way to improve the chances of having my letter read?

A. There are several things you can do. If the person is not listed in this book, try to find out where he or she works, write to that address and request that the mail be forwarded. If the person appears on radio or television, or in motion pictures or a magazine, write to the studio or editor, again requesting that the mail be forwarded. Be sure to include your name and address so that the notable can easily answer. You might even include a self-addressed, stamped envelope. Make it as easy as possible to read your letter — that is, it should be legible (typewritten or written in ink), and it should be as short and to the point as possible.

Q. What are the "don'ts" in writing to notables?

A. Don't send money ever! And don't send food. Don't wrap gifts in large boxes with lots of ribbon and yards of protective wrapping. Don't forget to include your name and address on all material you send.

Q. Do corporation heads pay attention to mail from a single individual?

A. Certainly! Most corporation heads are zealous in trying to find solutions to complaints. The old adage, "when you have a problem, go to the top," appears to be accurate. Company heads also enjoy and appreciate hearing the good news (satisfaction, extra service, a helpful employee).

Q. What about politicians? Are they really interested in what I have to say?

A. Of course. Politicians have a standard rule of thumb: for every letter received, they estimate that 100 people who *didn't* write are thinking the same thoughts as the letter expresses. So you can calculate the effect of your one letter as multiplied by 100.

Q. Do celebrities consider mail important?

A. Absolutely. Almost all notables keep a very close watch on their mail. It is a real indication of what people are thinking and feeling. Often the notable, surrounded by a small group of close associates, becomes isolated from the public. Your letter helps break down this isolation.

Q. What do most people say in their letters?

A. Most letters are very kind and full of compliments, sincere writings of what people would say if they had the opportunity. Infamous people and others who are out of favor with the general public predictably receive hostile, angry letters.

Q. What if my letter is returned to me?

A. Most of the people listed in this book are highly transient, changing addresses far more often than the average person. Their mail is usually forwarded to them, but occasionally a letter may be returned to the sender. If this should happen to your letter, first check to make sure you have copied the address correctly. If so you may mail *the returned envelope only* to the address below, along with a self-addressed stamped envelope. We will try to locate the new address of the notable and send it to you.

Michael Levine c/o Price/Stern/Sloan Publishers, Inc.
410 North La Cienega Boulevard, Los Angeles, California 90048

HOW TO USE THIS BOOK

Most of the entries in this book are names of persons notable in some area of endeavor. But you will also find many companies, agencies and institutions listed under the name of the organization. This is done so that you can find the address of IBM, for instance, without knowing the name of the president. The entry will then give you the address and the president's name.

How to Reach Anyone Who's Anyone is compiled alphabetically for easy reference. There are, however, two exceptions to this order:

*all the Bell System telephone companies are listed alphabetically in a separate group labeled **Telephone Companies** under "T;"*

*all the state utility commissions are listed alphabetically in a separate group labeled **Utility Commissions** under "U."*

Again, this has been done to make it easier to find the address and person you need.

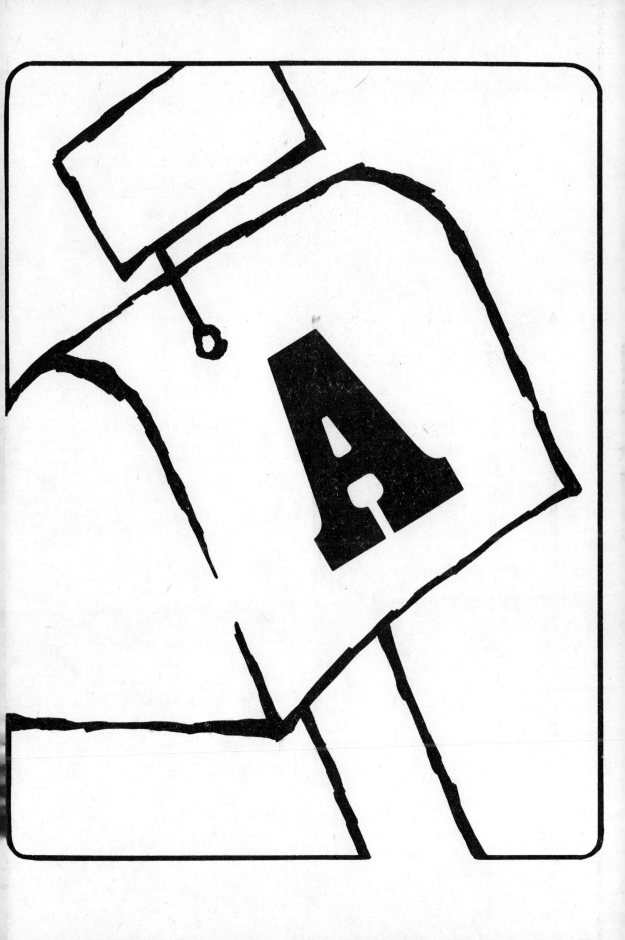

A & P Grocery Stores
2 Paragon Drive
Montvale, NJ 07645
Jonathan Scott, president

AMF Incorporated
777 Westchester Ave.
White Plains, NY 10604
W. Thomas York, president

Aamco Transmissions
408 E. 4th St.
Bridgeport, PA 19405
Robert Morgan, president

Aames, Willie
c/o ABC TV
4151 Prospect Ave.
Los Angeles, CA 90027
actor

Aaron, Hank
c/o Atlanta Braves
Atlanta Fulton County Stadium
Atlanta, Ga 30312
retired baseball player

Abbott, George
1270 Avenue of the Americas
New York, NY 10020
playwright

Abdul-Jabbar, Kareem (Lew Alcindor)
c/o LA Lakers
P.O. Box 10
Inglewood, CA 90306
basketball player

Abrahamsen, Samuel
4 Washington Square Village
New York, NY 10012
educator

Abzug, Bella
76 Beaver St.
New York, NY 10005
former congresswoman

Acheson, Mrs. Dean
2805 P St.
Washington DC 20037
widow of Dean Acheson

Acne Research Institute
1351 W. 16th St.
Miami, FL 33125
Anne Gathings, director

ACTION
806 Connecticut Ave. NW
Washington DC 20525
Sam Brown, director

Adair, Red
8705 Katy Freeway
Houston, TX 77024
firefighter

Adam, Ansel
Route 1, P.O. Box181
Carmel, CA 93923
photographer

Adams, Don
c/o David Licht
9171 Wilshire Blvd.
Beverly Hills, CA 90210
actor

Adams, Edie
c/o Henri Bollinger
3633 Crownridge Drive
Sherman Oaks, CA 91403
actress

Adams, Harriet (Carolyn Keene)
c/o Stratemeyer Syndicate
197 Maplewood Ave.
Maplewood, NJ 07400
author

Adams, John V.
200 Berkely St.
Boston, MA 02116
great-great-great grandson of President John Adams

Adolfo (Sardinia)
Adolfo Inc.
538 Madison Ave.
New York, NY 10021
fashion designer

Aetna Life & Casualty
151 Farmington Ave.
Hartford, CT 06115
John Filer, president

African Methodist Episcopal Church
P.O. Box 183
St. Louis, MO 63107
Dr. Richard Chappele, general secretary

Agee, Philip
c/o Melvin Wolf
565 5th Ave.
New York, NY 10022
author

Agnew, Spiro T.
c/o Pathlite Inc.
Village Green
Crofton, MA 21114
former vice-president

Ailey, Alvin
Alvin Ailey AM
Dance Theater
229 E. 59th St.
New York, NY 10022
choreographer

al-Ahmad al Sabah, Jaber Sheik
Office of Emir
Al-Kuwait, Kuwait
ruler of Kuwait

Al-Anon
1 Park Ave.
New York, NY 10016
Stephanie O'Keefe, chairperson

al-Assad, Hafez
Damascus, Syria
president of Syria

Alberghetti, Anna Maria
c/o Beakel-Jennings
427 N. Camden Drive
Beverly Hills, CA 90210
actress

Albert, Eddie
c/o ICM
8899 Beverly Blvd.
Los Angeles, CA 90048
actor

Albert, Edward Jr.
c/o ICPR
9255 Sunset Blvd.
Los Angeles, CA 90069
actor

Albertson, Jack
c/o Wm. Morris
151 El Camino Drive
Beverly Hills, CA 90212
actor

Alcoholics Anonymous World Services
P.O. Box 459
Grand Central Station
New York, NY 10016
Robert Pearson, general manager

Alda, Alan
c/o Wm. Morris
151 El Camino Drive
Beverly Hills, CA 90212
actor

Aldrich, Robert
201 N. Occidental Blvd.
Los Angeles, CA 90026
producer, director

Aldrin, Buzz
c/o Hillcrest Motors
9230 Wilshire Blvd.
Beverly Hills, CA 90212
former astronaut

Alexander, Donald
299 Park Ave.
New York, NY 10017
former IRS commissioner

Alexander, Jane
c/o ICM
40 W. 57th St.
New York, NY 10019
actress

Alexander, Lamar
Office of the Governor
Nashville, TN 37219
governor of Tennessee

Alexander, Shana
c/o CBS TV
524 W. 57th St.
New York, NY 10019
journalist

Ali, Muhammad
P.O. Box 53298
Chicago, IL 60653
world heavyweight boxing champion, actor

Allen, Betty Lou
Columbia Artists
Management Inc.
Ries Division
122 E. 66th St.
New York, NY 10019
mezzo-soprano

Allen, Irwin
c/o Warner Bros.
4000 Warner Blvd.
Burbank, CA 91522
producer, director

Allen, Lucius
c/o Kansas City Kings
Kemper Arena
1800 Genesee
Kansas City, MO 64102
basketball player

Allen, Mel
c/o NBC Sports
30 Rockefeller Plaza
New York, NY 10020
sportscaster

Allen, Peter
c/o A & M Records
1416 La Brea Ave.
Los Angeles, CA 90028
musician

Allen, Richard
c/o Oakland As
Oakland-Alameda
County Coliseum
Oakland, CA 94621
baseball player

Allen, Sandy
105 S. Hamilton
Shelbyville, IN 46176
*world's tallest living
woman (7'¼")*

Allen, Steve
15201 Burbank Blvd.
Van Nuys, CA 91401
writer, actor, comedian

Allen, Woody
930 5th Ave.
New York, NY 10021
*producer, director, writer,
actor*

Alliance to Save Energy
1925 K St. NW #507
Washington DC 20006
Linda Gallagher, director

Allied Chemical Co.
Columbia Road & Park Ave.
Morristown, NJ 07960
John Connor, president

Allman, Greg
535 Cotton Ave.
Macon, GA 31201
musician

Allstate Insurance Co.
Allstate Plaza
Northbrook, IL 60062
Archie Boe, president

Allyson, June
865 Comstock Ave.
Los Angeles, CA 90024
actress

Alpert, Herb
c/o A & M Records
1416 N. La Brea Ave.
Hollywood, CA 90028
musician

Alston, Walter
Route 2
Oxford, OH 45056
former baseball manager

Altman, Robert
c/o Lions Gate Productions
1334 Westwod Blvd.
Los Angeles, CA 90024
producer, director

Ameche, Don
c/o Burton Moss
113 San Vicente Blvd.
Beverly Hills, CA 90211
actor

America
c/o Hartman & Goodman
1500 Cross Roads of
the World
Los Angeles, CA 90028
music group

American Advertising Federation
1225 Connecticut Ave. NW
Washington DC 20036
Howard H. Bell, president

American Airlines
633 3rd Ave.
New York, NY 10017
Albert Casey, president

American Assn. of Advertising Agencies
200 Park Ave.
New York, NY 10017
William R. Hesse, president

American Broadcasting Co.
1330 Avenue of the Americas
New York, NY 10019
*Leonard Goldenson,
president*

American Civil Liberties Union
22 E. 40th St.
New York, NY 10016
Aryeh Neier, director

American Euthanasia Foundation
95 N. Birch Road, Suite 301
Ft. Lauderdale, FL 33304
Vincent F. Sullivan, president

American Express Company
American Express Plaza
New York, NY 10004
James Robinson III, president

American Federation of Nazi Victims
315 Lexington Ave.
New York, NY 10016
Solomon Zynstein, president

American Federation of Teachers
11 DuPont Circle
Washington DC 20036
Albert Shanker, president

American Greeting Card Company
10500 American Road
Cleveland, OH 44102
Morris Stone, president

American Hair Replacement Assn.
1422 K St. NW
Washington DC 20005
Dick Gibson, director

American Motors Corporation
14250 Plymouth Road
Detroit, MI 48232
Roy D. Chapin Jr., president

American Pencil Collectors
1227½ N. McLean
Lincoln, IL 62656
Richard G. Pearce, coordinator

American Red Cross
17th & D Sts.
Washington DC 20006
George M. Elsey, president

American Society for the Prevention of Cruelty to Animals
441 E. 92nd St.
New York, NY 10028
Dr. John F. Kullberg, director

American Venereal Disease Association
P.O. Box 385
University of
Virginia Hospital
Charlottesville, VA 22901
Michael Rein, director

American Youth Hostels
National Campus
Delaplane, VA 22025
Thomas L. Newman, director

Americans Against Abortion
6555 SW Lewis
Tulsa, OK 74102
Daniel Lyons, chairman

Amin, Idi
c/o Col. Muammar
el Qaddafe
Tripoli, Libya
deposed dictator of Uganda

Amnesty International
2112 Broadway Room 405
New York, NY 10023
David Hawk, director

Amos, John
c/o The Artists Agency
190 N. Canon Drive #320
Beverly Hills, CA 90210
actor

Amos, Wally
7181 Sunset Blvd.
Hollywood, CA 90028
creator of Famous Amos Cookies

Amsterdam, Morey
1012 N. Hillcrest Road
Beverly Hills, CA 90210
comedian

Amtrak
955 L'Enfant Plaza SW
Washington DC 20024
Paul Reistrup, president

Anderson, Bradley
1429 Pebble Beach
Yuma, AZ 85364
cartoonist ("Marmaduke")

Anderson, Ian
c/o Chrysalis Records
9255 Sunset Blvd.
Los Angeles, CA 90069
musician (Jethro Tull)

Anderson, Jack
1401 16th St. NW
Washington DC 20036
journalist

Anderson, John
Congress
Washington DC 20515
*U.S. representative,
presidential candidate*

Anderson, Loni
c/o Mickey Freeman
8732 Sunset Blvd. #250
Los Angeles, CA 90069
actress

Anderson, Lynn
c/o Penny Clevenger
P.O. Box 1962
Nashville, TN 37202
singer

Anderson, Marian
Danbury Court, CT 06810
singer

Andress, Ursula
c/o Kohner-Levy
9169 Sunset Blvd.
Los Angeles, CA 90069
actress

Andretti, Mario
53 Victory Lane
Nazareth, PA 18064
race driver

Andrews, Dana
Box B
Palos Verdes Peninsula,
CA 90274
actor

Andrews, Julie
c/o Regency Artists
9200 Sunset Blvd. Suite 823
Los Angeles, CA 90069
actress, singer

Angley, Ernest
Akron, OH 44309
evangelist

Angelou, Maya
P.O. Box
North Hot Springs, CA 94516
actress, author

Anka, Paul
c/o Paul Anka Productions
26070 Via Rivera
Carmel, CA 93923
entertainer

Annenberg, Walter
250 King of Prussia Road
Radnor, PA 19088
*publisher,
former ambassador*

Ann-Margret
c/o Solters & Roskin
9255 Sunset Blvd.
Los Angeles, CA 90069
entertainer, actress

**Anti-Communist
League of America**
3100 Park Suite 101
Newport Beach, CA 92660
John K. Crippen, director

**Antique Automobile
Club of America**
501 W. Governor Road
Hershey, PA 17033
*William E. Baumgardner,
manager*

Anton, Susan
c/o JNS Enterprises
9200 Sunset Blvd.
Los Angeles, CA 90069
entertainer

Arafat, Yassir
P.O. Box 145 168
Beirut, Lebanon
*leader, Palestine Liberation
Organization*

Arcaro, Eddie
c/o CBS Sports
51 W. 52nd St.
New York, NY 10019
sportscaster, former jockey

Archerd, Army
c/o *Daily Variety*
1400 N. Cahuenga Blvd.
Hollywood, CA 90028
entertainment columnist

**Arden, Elizabeth
Inc.**
1345 Avenue of the Americas
New York, NY 10019
*Joseph F. Ronchetti,
president*

Arden, Eve
P.O. Box 1065
Studio City, CA 90164
actress

Ariyoshi, George R.
Office of the Governor
Honolulu, HI 96813
governor of Hawaii

Arkin, Alan
c/o Robinson & Associates
132 S. Rodeo Drive
Beverly Hills, CA 90212
actor

Arledge, Roone
c/o ABC
1330 Avenue of the Americas
New York, NY 10019
*president, ABC news
and sports*

Armstrong, Anne
Armstrong Ranch
Armstrong, TX 78338
*member of board of directors
of General Motors,
former ambassador*

Armstrong, Del
3111 S. Barrington Ave.
Los Angeles, CA 90066
make-up artist

**Armstrong,
Ellis Leroy**
3709 Brockbank Drive
Salt Lake City, UT 84117
engineer

Armstrong, Neil
c/o College of Engineering
University of Cincinnati
Cincinnati, OH 45221
*former astronaut, first man
to walk on moon*

Armstrong, William
Senate Office Building
Washington DC 20510
senator from Colorado

Arnaz, Desi
c/o ICM
8899 Beverly Blvd.
Los Angeles, CA 90048
actor, producer

Arness, James
1456 N. Bronson Ave.
Hollywood, CA 90028
actor

Arnold, Danny
c/o Vine Street Studios
1313 Vine St.
Hollywood, CA 90028
producer, director

Arnold, Eddy
c/o Gerard W. Purcell
Associates
150 E. 52nd St.
New York, NY 10022
singer

Arnold, Richard M.
3420 Kitzmiller Road
New Albany, OH 43054
*heads radio search for
extraterrestrial intelligence*

Arrington, Richard
Office of the Mayor
City Hall
Birmingham, AL 35203
*first black mayor
of Birmingham*

Arritola, Paul
Police Headquarters
Jordan valley, OR 97910
*police chief who is allowed to
keep fines from speeding tic-
kets; earned over $100,000 in
1978*

Arthur, Beatrice
c/o Tandem Productions
1901 Avenue of the Stars
Los Angeles, CA 90067
actress

Ashby, Hal
c/o Greene & Reynolds
1900 Avenue of the Stars
Suite 1424
Los Angeles, CA 90067
producer, director

Asher, Peter
644 N. Doheny Drive
Los Angeles, CA 90069
talent manager, musician

Ashley, Elizabeth
c/o Agency for the
Performing Arts
9000 Sunset Blvd. Suite 315
Los Angeles, CA 90069
actress

Asimov, Isaac
10 W. 66th St. #33A
New York, NY 10023
author

Asner, Edward
c/o Jack Fields & Associates
9255 Sunset Blvd.
Los Angeles, CA 90069
actor

Association of Acrobats
23 Victor Road
Brookvale, N.S.W. 2100
Australia
R.P.H. Samuels, secretary

Astaire, Fred
c/o ICM
8899 Beverly Blvd.
Los Angeles, CA 90048
dancer, actor

Astin, John
P.O. Box 385
Beverly Hills, CA 90213
director, actor

Astor, Mary
Motion Picture
Country Home
23450 Calabasas Road
Woodland Hills, CA 91334
actress

Atherton, Alfred
Dept. of State
Washington DC 20024
foreign service officer

Atiyeh, Victor
Office of the Governor
Salem, OR 97310
governor of Oregon

Atkins, Chet
806 17th Ave. S.
Nashville, TN 37203
musician

Atlantic Richfield Company
515 S. Flower St.
Los Angeles, CA 90071
R.O. Anderson, president

Auerbach, "Red"
Boston Celtics
North Stadium
Boston, MA 02114
basketball executive

Austin, Tracy
c/o Dell, Craighill
888 17th St. NW Suite 1700
Washington DC 20006
tennis player

Autry, Gene
c/o Golden West
Broadcasters
5858 Sunset Blvd.
Hollywood, CA 90028
*broadcasting and sports
executive, former singer*

Avalon, Frankie
865 Comstock
Los Angeles, CA 90024
singer, actor

Avedon, Richard
407 E. 75th St.
New York, NY 10021
photographer

Avildsen, John
45 E.89th St.
New York, NY 10028
film director

Avis Rent-A-Car
900 Old Country Road
Garden City, NY 11530
Colin Marshall, president

Avon Company
9 W. 57th St.
New York, NY 10019
David Mitchell, president

Axelrod, George
301 N. Carolwood Drive
Los Angeles, CA 90024
playwright

Axton, Hoyt
P.O. Box 614
Tahoe City, CA 95730
musician

Ayckbourne, Alan
c/o Chatto & Jonathin Cape
Ltd.
9 Bow St.
London WC2 E1AL
England
playwright

Aykroyd, Dan
c/o Bernie Brillstein
9200 Sunset Blvd.
Los Angeles, CA 90069
actor

Aznavour, Charles
4 Ave. de Lieulee
78 Galluis, France
singer, composer

Babbitt, Bruce
1700 W. Washington
Phoenix, AZ 85007
head of presidential committee which investigated Three Mile Island; governor of Arizona

Babilonia, Tai
102-09 Norwich Ave.
Mission Hills, CA 91340
figure skater

Bacall, Lauren
c/o Peter Witt Associates
37 W. 57th St.
New York, NY 10019
actress

Bach, Barbara
c/o Creative Artists Agency
1888 Century Park E.
Suite 1400
Los Angeles, CA 90067
actress

Bacharach, Burt
c/o ICM
8899 Beverly Blvd.
Los Angeles, CA 90048
musician, composer

Bacheller, Martin A.
Hammond Almanac
Maplewood, NJ 07040
editor-in-chief

Bachrach, Bradford
44 Hunt St.
Watertown, MA 02172
photographer

Bachrach, Louis Fabian Jr.
44 Hunt St.
Watertown, MA 02172
photographer

Backus, Jim
8810 Sunset Blvd.
Los Angeles, CA 90069
actor

Baer, Max
109 N. La Cienega Blvd.
Los Angeles, CA 90048
actor

Baez, Joan
c/o Chandos Productions
P.O. Box 1026
Menlo Park, CA 94025
singer

Bailar, Benjamin F.
475 L' Enfant Plaza SW
Washington DC 20250
postmaster general

Bailey, A.A. "Paddy"
P.O. Box 391
5910 Mineral Point Road
Madison, WI 53701
director, World Council of Credit Unions

Bailey, F. Lee
1 Center Plaza
Boston, MA 02108
attorney

Bailey, Pearl
c/o Wm. Morris
1350 Avenue of the Americas
New York, NY 10019
entertainer

Bain, Barbara
c/o Creative Artists Agency
1888 Century Park E.
Suite 1400
Los Angeles, CA 90067
actress

Baio, Scott
c/o ABC TV
4151 Prospect Ave.
Los Angeles, CA 90027
actor

Baird, Bill
59 Barrow St.
New York, NY 10014
puppeteer

Baker, Bobby
c/o W.W. Norton
500 5th Ave.
New York, NY 10036
former Johnson aide

Baker, Howard
Senate Office Building
Washington DC 20510
senator from Tennessee

Baker, Joe Don
23339 Hatteras St.
Woodland Hills, CA 91364
actor

Baker, Dr. R.R.
Johns Hopkins Hospital
601 N. Broadway
Baltimore, MD 21205
surgeon specializing in breast cancer

Baker St. Irregulars
33 Riverside Drive
New York, NY 10023
literary society devoted to study of Sherlock Holmes; Julian Wolff, director

Baker, William Oliver
Spring Valley Road
Morristown, NJ 07960
research chemist

Balanchine, George
144 W. 66th St.
New York, NY 10023
choreographer

Bald-Headed Men of America
P.O. Box "BALD"
Dunn, NC 28334
John T. Capps III, executive director

Baldwin, James
c/o Dial Press
1 Dag Hammarskjold Plaza
245 E 47th St.
New York, NY 10017
author

Baldwin Piano & Organ Co.
Baldwin-United Corp.
1801 Gilbert Ave.
Cincinnati, OH 45202
Lucien Wulsin, president

Ball, Lucille
c/o Lucille Ball Productions
Universal Studios
Universal City, CA 91608
entertainer

Ballantine, Ian
c/o Ballantine Books
Bearsville, NY 12409
publisher

Ballard, Kaye
c/o Richard Francis
328 S. Beverly Drive #A
Beverly Hills, CA 90212
singer

Balsam, Martin
c/o Robinson & Associates
132 S. Rodeo Drive
Beverly Hills, CA 90212
actor

Bancroft, Anne
c/o Howard Rothberg Ltd.
1706 N. Doheny Drive
Los Angeles, CA 90069
actress

Bank of America
Bank of America Center
San Francisco, CA 94137
A.W. Clausen, president

Banks, Ernie
c/o Chicago Cubs
Wrigley Field
N. Clark & Addison Sts.
Chicago, IL 60613
former baseball player

Banzhaf, John
P.O. Box 19556
Washington DC 20006
president of ASH (Action on Smoking and Health – non-smokers lobby group)

Barbeau, Adrienne
c/o Rush/Flaherty Agency
10889 Wilshire Blvd.
Suite 1130
Los Angeles, CA 90024
actress

Barbera, Joseph
c/o Hanna-Barbera Productions
3400 W. Cahuenga Blvd.
Hollywood, CA 90068
animated film producer

Barcelo, Carlos Romero
Office of the Governor
San Juan, Puerto Rico 00902
governor of Puerto Rico

Bardot, Brigitte
71 Avenue Paul-Doumer
Paris 16, France
actress

Baretski, Charles Allan
229 Montclair Ave.
Newark, NJ 07104
librarian, political scientist, historian

Barnes, Clive
c/o *New York Post*
210 South St.
New York, NY 10002
drama critic

Barrett, Rona
7060 Hollywood Blvd.
Suite 800
Hollywood, CA 90028
columnist

Barris, Chuck
c/o Chuck Barris Productions
6430 Sunset Blvd.
Hollywood, CA 90028
producer

Barrows, Marjorie
1615 Hinman Ave.
Evanston, IL 60201
author

Barry, Gene
622 N. Maple Drive
Beverly Hills, CA 90210
actor

Barstow, Richard
200 W. 54th St.
New York, NY 10019
choreographer

Baryshnikov, Mikhail
c/o Edgar Vincent Associates
156 E. 52nd St.
New York, NY 10022
dancer

Basehart, Richard
9470 Lloydcrest
Beverly Hills, CA 90210
actor

Basie, Count
c/o Willard Alexander Inc.
660 Madison Ave.
New York, NY 10021
musician, conductor

Baskin-Robbins
31 Baskin-Robbins Place
Glendale, CA 91201
Robert J. Hudecek, president

Bassey, Shirley
Via Torengo, 6 Lugano
Switzerland
singer

Battelle, Kenneth
c/o Kenneth Salon
19 E. 54th St.
New York, NY 10022
hairdresser

Battley, Larry
2780 N. Quincy St.
Arlington, VA 22207

Amtrack executive, private railroad car leaser

Baucus, Max
Senate Office Building
Washington DC 20510
senator from Montana

Baxter, Anne
c/o Chasin-Park-Citron
9255 Sunset Blvd.
Los Angeles, CA 90069
actress

Baxter-Birney, Meredith
c/o Jack Fields & Associates
9255 Sunset Blvd.
Suite 1105
Los Angeles, CA 90069
actress

Bay City Rollers
c/o Tom Paton
Abbott House 1 & 2
Hanover St.
London
England WIR 9WB
music group

Bayh, Birch
Senate Office Building
Washington DC 20510
senator from Indiana

Beach Boys
3621 Sepulveda Blvd. #3
Manhattan Beach, CA 90266
music group

Beame, Abe
250 Broadway
New York, NY 10007
former mayor of New York City

Bean, Orson
910 Chatauqua
Pacific Palisades, CA 90272
entertainer

Bear, Yogi
c/o Hanna Barbera
Productions
3400 Cahuenga Blvd.
Hollywood, CA 90068
cartoon character

Beard, James
167 W. 12th St.
New York, NY 10011
author

Beatty, Ned
c/o Jack Fields & Associates
9255 Sunset Blvd.
Suite 1105
Los Angeles, CA 90069
actor

Beatty, Warren
c/o William Morris
151 El Camino Drive
Beverly Hills, CA 90212
actor

Beck, Marilyn
P.O. Box 655
Beverly Hills, CA 90213
*world's most syndicated
entertainment columnist*

Bedelia, Bonnie
c/o The Artists Agency
190 N. Canon Drive
Beverly Hills, CA 90210
actress

Bee Gees
c/o The Robert Stigwood
Organization
1775 Broadway
New York, NY 10019
music group

Beene, Geoffrey
c/o Geoffrey Beene Inc.
550 7th Ave.
New York, NY 10018
fashion designer

Begelman, David
c/o MGM
10202 Washington Blvd.
Culver City, CA 90230
president, MGM

Begin, Menachem
Office of the Prime Minister
Jerusalem, Israel
prime minister of Israel

Bekins Moving Co.
1335 S. Figueroa St.
Los Angeles, CA 90015
Milo Bekins Jr., president

Belafonte, Harry
c/o Belafonte Enterprises Inc.
157 W. 57th St.
New York, NY 10019
singer

Bel Geddes, Barbara
c/o Lorimar Productions
10202 Washington Blvd.
Culver City, CA 90230
actress

Bell & Howell Co.
7100 McCormick Road
Chicago, IL 60645
Donald Frey, president

Bellamy, Ralph
116 E. 27th St.
New York, NY 10016
actor

Belli, Melvin
1228 Montgomery St.
San Francisco, CA 94133
attorney

Bellmon, Henry L.
Senate Office Building
Washington DC 20510
senator from Oklahoma

Bellow, Saul
University of Chicago
Chicago, IL 60637
author

Belushi, John
c/o Bernie Brillstein
9200 Sunset Blvd.
Los Angeles, CA 90069
actor

Bench, Johnny
704 First National Bank Blvd.
Cincinnati, OH 45202
baseball player

Benchley, Peter
c/o Doubleday & Co.
245 Park Ave.
New York, NY 10017
author

Benedict, Dirk
c/o Stone Associates
8489 W. 3rd St.
Los Angeles, CA 90048
actor

Benjamin, Richard
c/o Phil Gersh Agency
222 N. Canon Drive
Beverly Hills, CA 90210
actor

Benji
c/o Mulberry Square
Productions
10300 N. Central
Expressway #120
Dallas, TX 75231
canine actor

Benko, Paul
73 Garrison Ave.
Atlantic City, NJ 07306
chess grand master

Bennett, Joan
67 Chase Road N.
Scarsdale, NY 10583
actress

Bennett, Michael
445 Park Ave.
New York, NY 10022
producer

Bennett, Tony
c/o Rollins, Joffe & Morra
130 W. 57th St.
New York, NY 10019
singer

Bennett, Wallace
875 Donner Way
Salt Lake City, UT 84108
former senator

Benny, Mrs. Jack
10231 Charing Cross Road
Los Angeles, CA 90024
widow of Jack Benny

Benson, George
c/o Warner Bros. Records
3000 Warner Blvd.
Burbank, CA 91510
singer, musician

Benson, Robby
c/o Wm. Morris
151 El Camino Drive
Beverly hills, CA 90212
actor

Bentley, Stacey
Sports Inc.
9665 Wilshire Blvd.
Beverly Hills, CA 90212
*women's body-building
champion*

Benton, Barbie
c/o Thames Talent Agency
1345 Avenue of the Americas
New York, NY 10019
actress

Bentsen, Lloyd
Senate Office Building
Washington DC 20510
senator from Texas

Berenson, Marisa
c/o ICM
40 W. 57th St.
New York, NY 10019
actress

Bergen, Candice
c/o ICM
8899 Beverly Blvd.
Los Angeles, CA 90048
actress

Bergen, Polly
8730 Sunset Blvd. Suite 401
Los Angeles, CA 90069
actress, designer

Bergeron, Victor
20 Cosmo Place
San Francisco, CA 94109
restaurateur (Trader Vic's)

Bergman, Alan & Marilyn
c/o Freedman & Freedman
911 Gateway West
Los Angeles, CA 90067
lyricists

Bergman, Ingmar
Svensk Filmindustri
Kungsgatan 36
Stockholm, Sweden
director

Bergman, Ingrid
c/o ICM
11-12 Hanover St.
London W1, England
actress

Berkowitz, David
c/o Attica State Prison
Attica, NY 14011
"Son of Sam"

Berle, Milton
c/o Irwin H. Rosenberg
430 Park Ave.
New York, NY 10022
comedian

Berlin, Irving
1290 6th Ave.
New York, NY 10009
composer

Bernstein, Carl
2853 Ontario Road NW
Washington DC 20009
investigative reporter

Bernstein, Elmer
Winter River Ranch
Malibu, CA 90265
composer

Bernstein, Leonard
205 W. 57th St.
New York, NY 10019
conductor, composer

Bernstein, Sid
1260 Avenue of the Americas
New York, NY 10020
impresario who brought the Beatles to America

Berra, "Yogi"
Sutherland Road
Montclair, NJ 07042
former baseball player

Berrigan, Daniel
220 W. 98th St.
New York, NY 10025
peace activist

Berrigan, Philip
1546 N. Fremont Ave.
Baltimore, MD 21217
peace activist

Berry, Chuck
c/o Bob Astor Management
23 Holly Drive
Los Angeles, CA 90068
musician

Berry, John
3170 Kettering Blvd.
Dayton, OH 45439
publisher of the Yellow Pages

Berti, Humberto Calderon
Energy Ministry
Caracas, Venezuela
president of OPEC

Bertinelli, Valerie
c/o CBS TV
7800 Beverly Blvd.
Los Angeles, CA 90036
actress

Biden, Joseph R. Jr.
Senate Office Bldg.
Washington DC 20510
senator from Delaware

Big Bird
c/o Children's Television Workshop
1 Lincoln Plaza
New York, NY 10022
television character

Big Brothers/Big Sisters of America
220 Suburban Station Bldg.
Philadelphia, PA 19103
L.P. Reade, executive vice-president

Bigge, William R.
Burtonville, MD 20730
world's record for flying most kites with one string – 261

Bikel, Theodore
Honey Mill Road
Georgetown, CT 06829
actor

Bill, Mr.
c/o NBC TV
30 Rockefeller Plaza
New York, NY 10022
TV character

Binney & Smith Crayola Company
2035 Edgewood Ave.
Easton, PA 18082
Russell McChesney, president

Bird, Rose
350 McAllister St.
San Francisco, CA 94102
chief justice, California Supreme Court

Birney, David
c/o Zeiderman
9200 Sunset Blvd.
Los Angeles, CA 90069
actor

Bishop, Joey
c/o Wm. Morris
151 El Camino Drive
Beverly Hills, CA 90212
entertainer

Bisset, Jacqueline
c/o ICM
8899 Beverly Blvd.
Los Angeles, CA 90048
actress

Bixby, Bill
c/o Brandon & Rogers
Associates
9046 Sunset Blvd. Suite 201
Los Angeles, CA 90069
actor

Bjerke, Eivind
Lucien et Eivind
22-33 Wisconsin Ave.
Washington DC 20007
*Rosalynn Carter's
hairdresser*

**Black & Decker Tool
Company**
701 E. Joppa Road
Towson, MD 21204
Alonzo Decker Jr., president

**Black, Shirley
Temple**
Woodside, CA 94062
*former actress, former
ambassador*

Blackmun, Harry
U.S. Supreme Court
Washington DC 20543
justice

**Blackstone,
Harry Jr.**
265 N. Robertson Blvd.
Beverly Hills, CA 90211
magician

Blair, Linda
c/o Wm. Morris
151 El Camino Drive
Beverly Hills, CA 90212
actress

Blake, Amanda
c/o Grossman-Stalmaster
Agency
8730 Sunset Blvd. Suite 405
Los Angeles, CA 90069
actress

Blake, Eubie
284 A Stuyvesant Ave.
Brooklyn, NY 11221
musician

Blake, Robert
c/o Universal Studios
Universal City, CA 91608
actor

Blakely, Susan
c/o Agency for the
Performing Arts
120 W. 57th St.
New York, NY 10019
actress

Blass, Bill
550 7th Ave.
New York, NY 10018
fashion designer

Blatty, William
c/o Harper & Row
10 E. 53rd St.
New York, NY 10022
author

Bloch, Henry
4410 Main St.
Kansas City, MO 64111
president, H & R Bloch

Bloch, Richard
4410 Main St.
Kansas City, MO 64111
chairman, H & R Bloch

Blondie
c/o King Features
235 E. 45th St.
New York, NY 10017
comic strip character

Bloom, Claire
c/o Aaron Frosch
445 Park Ave.
New York, NY 10022
actress

**Bloomingdales
Dept. Store**
1000 3rd Ave.
New York, NY 10022
Marvin Traub, president

Blue, Vida
c/o Oakland As
Oakland-Alameda County
Coliseum
Oakland, CA 94621
baseball player

Blume, Judy
c/o Bradbury Press
2 Overhill Road
Scarsdale, NY 10583
author

Bogart, Neil
8255 Sunset Blvd.
Los Angeles, CA 90046
*president, Casablanca
Records & Film Works*

Bogdanovich, Peter
c/o Saticoy Productions/
Copa de Oro Productions
300 Colgems Square
Burbank, CA 91505
director

Bolger, Ray
c/o Wm. Morris
151 El Camino Drive
Beverly Hills, CA 90212
actor

Bombeck, Erma
6301 N. 38th St.
Paradise Valley, AZ 85253
columnist

Bondurant, Bob
Bob Bondurant School of
High Performance Driving
Sears Point International
Raceway
Sonoma, CA 95476
race driver, teacher

Bonner, William
325 Pennsylvania Ave. SE
Washington DC 20003
*director, National
Taxpayers Union*

Bono, Sonny
c/o Wm. Morris
151 El Camino Drive
Beverly Hills, CA 90212
entertainer

**Book of the Month
Club**
280 Park Ave.
New York, NY 10024
Axel Rosin, president

Boone, Debby
c/o ICM
8899 Beverly Blvd.
Los Angeles, CA 90048
singer

Boone, Pat
c/o ICM
8899 Beverly Blvd.
Los Angeles, CA 90048
singer

Booth, Shirley
10329 Eastbourne St.
Los Angeles, CA 90024
actress

Boren, David L.
Senate Office Building
Washington DC 20510
senator from Oklahoma

Borg, Bjorn
c/o International
Management Group
1 Erieview Plaza
Cleveland, OH 44114
tennis player

Borge, Victor
Field Point Park
Greenwich, CT 06830
entertainer

Borgnine, Ernest
c/o APA
9000 Sunset Blvd.
Los Angeles, CA 90069
actor

Boschwitz, Rudy
Senate Office Building
Washington DC 20510
senator from Minnesota

Bosley, Tom
c/o Burton Moses Agency
118 S. Beverly Drive
Beverly Hills. CA 90212
actor

Boston
c/o Pure Management
1289 N. Crescent Heights
Blvd. Suite 303
Los Angeles, CA 90046
music group

Bottoms, Timothy
1783 Las Canoas
Santa Barbara, CA 93105
actor

Bouton, Jim
Maple St.
Englewood, NJ 07631
*author, former
baseball player*

Bowen, Otis R.
Office of the Governor
Indianapolis, IN 46204
governor of Indiana

Bowie, David
c/o RCA Records
1133 Avenue of the Americas
New York, NY 10036
singer

Boxleitner, Bruce
c/o MGM TV
10202 W. Washington Blvd.
Culver City, CA 90067
actor

Boy Scouts of America
North Brunswick, NJ 08902
*Harvey L. Price,
chief executive*

Boyle, Peter
c/o Creative Artists Agency
1888 Century Park E.
Suite 1400
Los Angeles, CA 90067
actor

Boyle, Tony
c/o Charles Peruto
NE Corner 8th & Locust Sts.
Philadelphia, PA 19106
*former United Mine Workers
president*

Bracken, Peg
56 Kahana Place
Lahaina, Maui HI 96761
author

Bradley, Bill
Senate Office Building
Washington DC 20510
*senator from New Jersey,
former basketball player*

Bradley, Tom
City Hall
Los Angeles, CA 90012
mayor of Los Angeles

Bradshaw, Terry
Commercial National Bank
Building #1012
Shreveport, LA 71101
football player

Braka, Carl
c/o David McKay
750 3rd Ave.
New York, NY 10017
*author; expert
on charities*

Bramel, G.
P.O. Box 44
Washington, KY 41906
*organizer of frog jumping
contest*

Brando, Marlon
P.O. Box 809
Beverly Hills, CA 90213
actor

Braniff Airways
Braniff Aviation Building
Dallas, TX 75232
*Harding L. Lawrence,
president*

Brautigan, Richard
c/o Simon & Schuster
630 5th Ave.
New York, NY 10020
author

Brenda, Mike
P.O. Box 6201
Pasadena, TX 77506
leader, American Nazi Party

Brennan, Eileen
c/o Creative Artists Agency
1888 Century Park E.
Suite 1400
Los Angeles, CA 90067
actress

Brennan, Frank
14 Roxbury Downs
Upper Saddle River,
NJ 07458
celebrity tennis teacher

Brennan, Joseph E.
Office of the Governor
Augusta, ME 04330
governor of Maine

Brennan, William
U.S. Supreme Court
Washington DC 20543
justice

Brenner, David
c/o Wm. Morris
1350 Avenue of the Americas
New York, NY 10019
comedian

Breslin, Jimmy
c/o *The Daily News*
220 E. 42nd St.
New York, NY 10017
journalist

Brezhnev, Leonid
Central Committee of the
Communist Party
4 Staraya Ploshchad
Moscow, USSR
Soviet chairman

Bridges, Beau
c/o Wm. Morris
151 El Camino Drive
Beverly Hills, CA 90212
actor

Bridges, Jeff
c/o ICM
8899 Beverly Blvd.
Los Angeles, CA 90048
actor

Bridges, Lloyd
c/o ICM
8899 Beverly Blvd.
Los Angeles, CA 90048
actor

Briggs, John
4141 N. Harbor Blvd.
Fullerton, CA 92268
anti-homosexual crusader

Brinkley, David
4001 Nebraska Ave. NW
Washington DC 20016
journalist

Brinks Armored Car Service
234 E. 24th St.
Chicago, IL 60616
Edgar Jones, president

Broccoli, Albert "Cubby"
315 S. Beverly Drive
Suite 500
Beverly Hills, CA 90210
producer

Brock, Alice
Alice's at Avaloch
Lenox, MA 01240
restaurateur (Alice's Restaurant)

Brock, Lou
c/o St. Louis Cardinals
Busch Memorial Stadium
250 Stadium Plaza
St. Louis, MO 63102
baseball player

Broderick, James
27 Washington Square N.
New York, NY 10011
actor

Brokaw, Tom
c/o NBC TV
30 Rockefeller Plaza
New York, NY 10020
journalist

Brolin, James
c/o Universal Pictures
100 Universal City Plaza
Universal City, CA 91608
actor

Bronson, Charles
c/o Kohner-Levy Agency
9169 Sunset Blvd.
Los Angeles, CA 90069
actor

Brooks, Foster
18116 Chadron Circle
Encino, CA 91316
comedian, actor

Brooks, Mel
c/o Howard Rothberg Ltd.
1706 N. Doheny Drive
Los Angeles, CA 90069
director, writer, actor

Brothers, Dr. Joyce
1530 Palisade Ave.
Fort Lee, NJ 07024
psychologist

Brown, Charlie
c/o United Feature Syndicate
200 Park Ave.
New York, NY 10017
comic strip character

Brown, Edmund Jr. (Jerry)
Office of the Governor
State Capitol
Sacramento, CA 95814
governor of California

Brown, Edmund Sr. (Pat)
450 N. Roxbury Drive
Beverly Hills, CA 90210
former governor of California

Brown, Helen Gurley
c/o Hearst Corporation
959 8th Ave.
New York, NY 10019
editor-in-chief, Cosmopolitan

Brown, James
Clifton & Denison Sts.
Baltimore, MD 21216
singer

Brown, Jim
c/o Charter Management
9000 Sunset Blvd.
Los Angeles, CA 90069
actor, former football player

Brown, John Y.
Office of the Governor
Frankfort, KY 40601
governor of Kentucky

Brown, Louise
Bristol, England
first test-tube baby

Browne, Dik
85 Rivergate Road
Wilton, CT 06898
cartoonist

Browne, Jackson
c/o Wm. Morris
151 El Camino Drive
Beverly Hills, CA 90212
singer

Browne, Leslie
c/o American Ballet Theatre
888 7th Ave.
New York, NY 10019
ballerina

Brownmiller, Susan
61 Jane St.
New York, NY 10014
feminist leader

Brubeck, Dave
c/o Derry Music Co.
240 Stockton St.
San Francisco, CA 94108
musician

Bruce, Jeffrey
1526 Walnut St.
Philadelphia, PA 19102
private beauty consultant to jet set

Brunswick Leisure Product Company
1 Brunswick Plaza
Skokie, IL 60076
K. Brooks Abernathy, president

Bryan, John Jr.
135 S. La Salle St.
Chicago, IL 60603
president, Consolidated Food Company

Bryant, Anita
c/o Bob Green Productions
925 Arthur Godfrey Road
Miami Beach, FL 33140
entertainer

Brynner, Yul
c/o Kohner-Levy Agency
9169 Sunset Blvd.
Los Angeles, CA 90069
actor

Brzezinski, Zbigniew
The White House
Washington DC 20500
national security adviser

Bucher, Lloyd
Poway, CA 92064
commander of the Pueblo

Buchwald, Art
1750 Pennsylvania Ave. NW #1311
Washington DC 20006
columnist

Buck, Jorge
Research Center of Microbial Ecology
C.P. 1428, Obligado 2490
Buenos Aires, Argentina
transformed 20,000 sq. kilometers of previously unproductive land into producing farmland

Buckley, William J.
150 E. 35th St.
New York, NY 10016
columnist

Bugliosi, Vincent
9171 Wilshire Blvd.
Beverly Hills, CA 90210
prosecutor in the Manson case

Bukovsky, Vladimir
c/o Amnesty International USA
2112 Broadway
New York, NY 10023
Soviet dissident

Bulova Watch Company Ltd.
Bulova Park
Flushing, NY 11370
Harry Bulova Henshel, mfr.

Bumpers, Dale
Senate Office Bldg.
Washington DC 20510
senator from Arkansas

Bunny, Bugs
c/o Warner Bros. TV
4000 Warner Blvd.
Burbank, CA 91505
cartoon character

Burdick, Quentin,
Senate Office Building
Washington DC 20510
senator from North Dakota

Burger King
7360 N. Kendall Drive
Miami, FL 33152
Winston R. Wallin, president

Burger, Warren
Supreme Court Building
Washington DC 20543
chief justice

Burgess, Anthony
44 rue Grimaldi
Monte Carlo, Monaco
author

Burghoff, Gary
c/o Belson & Klass Associates
211 S. Beverly Drive
Beverly Hills, CA 90212
actor

Burke, Dr. J.F.
Shriner's Hospital for Crippled Children
Boston, MA 02114
pediatric burn specialist

Burke, Yvonne Braithwaite
1 Manchester Road
Inglewood, CA 90301
Los Angeles County supervisor

Burnett, Carol
c/o Robinson & Associates
132 S. Rodeo Drive
Beverly Hills, CA 90212
actress, entertainer

Burnham, Forbes
Office of the Prime Minister
Georgetown, Guyana
prime minister of Guyana

Burns, George
c/o Irving Fein
1100 Alta Loma Road
Los Angeles, CA 90069
actor, entertainer

Burns Security Service
320 Old Briarcliffe Road
Briarcliffe Manor, NY 10510
Frederic Crist, president

Burr, Raymond
c/o ICPR
9255 Sunset Blvd.
Los Angeles, CA 90069
actor

Burroughs, Robert
1015 Elm St.
Manchester, NH 03101
pioneer designer of pension plans

Burrows, Abe
c/o Wm. Morris
1350 Avenue of the Americas
New York, NY 10019
playwright

Burrows, Stephen
550 7th Ave.
New York, NY 10018
fashion designer

Burstyn, Ellen
c/o Wm. Morris
1350 Avenue of the Americas
New York, NY 10019
actress

Burton, LeVar
c/o Wm. Morris
151 El Camino Drive
Beverly Hills, CA 90212
actor

Burton, Richard
c/o John Springer Associates
667 Madison Ave,
New York, NY 10021
actor

Busbee, George
Office of the Governor
Atlanta, GA 30334
governor of Georgia

Busby, Jim
c/o ICPR
9255 Sunset Blvd.
Los Angeles, CA 90069
race car driver

Busch, August
721 Pestalozzi St.
St. Louis, MO 63118
president, Anheuser-Busch Inc. & St. Louis Cardinals

Busey, Gary
c/o Mishkin Agency
9255 Sunset Blvd.
Los Angeles, CA 90069
actor

Butkus, Dick
c/o David Shapira
& Associates
9171 Wilshire Blvd.
Suite 525
Beverly Hills, CA 90210
actor, former football player

Butterfield, Alexander
3 Brent Court
Menlo Park, CA 94025
person who revealed Watergate tapes

Button, Dick
c/o ABC Sports
1330 Avenue of the Americas
New York, NY 10019
figure skating commentator

Buttons, Red
c/o Contemporary-Korman Artists
132 Lasky Drive
Beverly Hills, CA 90212
entertainer, actor

Butz, Earl
321 Jefferson Drive W.
Lafayette, IN 47906
former secretary of agriculture

Buzzi, Ruth
c/o Wm. Morris
151 El Camino Drive
Beverly Hills, CA 90212
comedienne

Byrd, Harry F. Jr.
Senate Office Building
Washington DC 20510
senator from Virginia

Byrd, Robert C.
Senate Office Building
Washington DC 20510
senator from West Virginia

Byrne, Brendan T.
Office of the Governor
Trenton, NJ 08625
governor of New Jersey

Byrne, Jane
City Hall
121 N. LaSalle St.
Chicago, IL 60602
mayor of Chicago

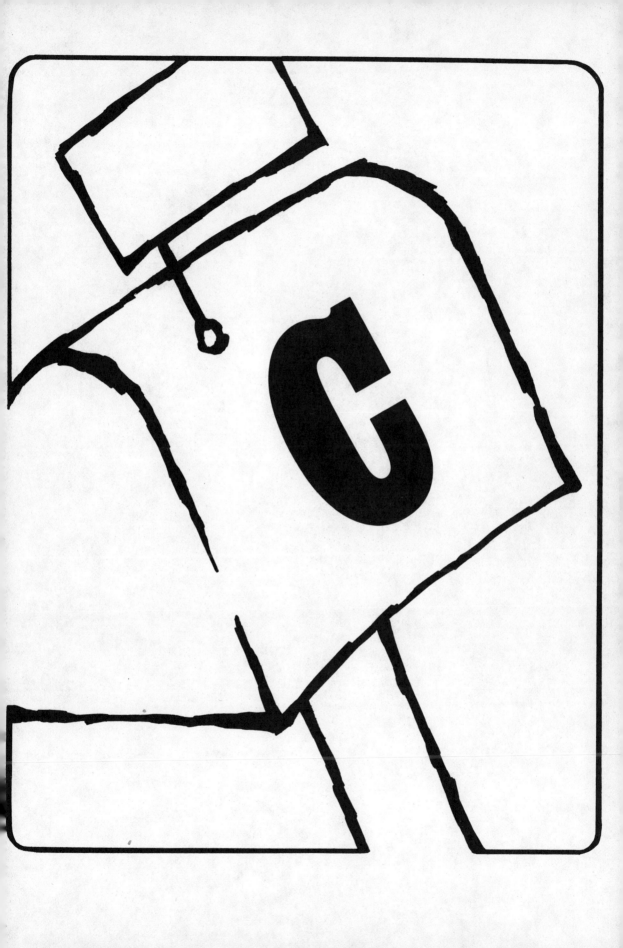

C3PO (Cee Three P O)
c/o Lucasfilms
P.O. Box 8669
Universal City, CA 91608
robot

Caan, James
c/o Wm. Morris
151 El Camino Drive
Beverly Hills, CA 90212
actor

Cadillac Motor Cars Company
2860 Clark Ave.
Detroit, MI 48232
Edward Kennard, president

Cady, Dr. B.
Lahey Clinic
Boston, MA 02166
surgeon – specialist in breast cancer

Caesar, Sid
c/o Contemporary-Korman Artists
132 Lasky Drive
Beverly Hills, CA 90212
entertainer

Cagney, James
2069 Coldwater Canyon
Beverly Hills, CA 90210
actor

Cahill, William T.
P.O. Box 1447
Camden, NJ 08101
former New Jersey governor

Cahn, Sammy
c/o Traubner & Flynn
1800 Century Park E.
Los Angeles, CA 90067
lyricist

Caine, Michael
912 N. Roxbury Drive
Beverly Hills, CA 90210
actor

Caldwell, Janet
34 Audley Road
Buffalo, NY 14226
author

Call For Action
1601 Connecticut Ave. NW
Suite 780
Washington DC 20009
Sandra J. Brown, director of consumer information clearing-house

Callaway, Howard H.
Crested Butte, CO 81224
former secretary of the army

Calley, William L.Jr.
c/o American Program Bureau
850 Boylston St.
Brookline, MA 02167
convicted in My Lai case

Calloway, Cab
c/o ICM
8899 Beverly Blvd.
Los Angeles, CA 90210
actor

Campanella, Joseph
c/o Blake Agency Ltd.
409 N. Camden Drive
Beverly Hills, CA 90210
actor

Campbell, Glen
P.O. Box 69500
Hollywood, CA 90069
singer

Campbell, Richard
P.O. Box 787
Jensen Beach, FL 33457
organizer of viking boat races

Campbell Soup Co.
Campbell Place
Camden, NJ 08101
John Dorrance, president

Canada Dry Soda Company
100 Park Ave.
New York, NY 10017
Richard Beeson, president

Cannon, Dyan
c/o Creative Artists Agency
1888 Century Park E.
Suite 1400
Los Angeles, CA 90067
actress

Cannon, Howard W.
Senate Office Building
Washington DC 20510
senator from Nevada

Canova, Diana
c/o Rifkin-David
9301 Wilshire Blvd.
Beverly Hills, CA 90210
actress

Canova, Judy
c/o Don Schwartz
& Associates
8721 Sunset Blvd.
Los Angeles, CA 90069
actress

Cantrell, Lana
300 E. 71st St.
New York, NY 10021
singer

Capote, Truman
Twin Towers
UN Plaza
New York, NY 10017
author

Capra, Frank
P.O. Box 98
La Quinta, CA 92253
producer, director

Capricorn Records
535 Cotton Ave.
Macon, GA 31201
Phil Walden, president

**Captain & Tennille
(Daryl Dragon &
Toni Tennille)**
c/o A & M Records
1416 N. La Brea Ave.
Los Angeles, CA 90028
singers

Cardin, Pierre
118 rue du Fauborg
Saint-Honore Paris 8e
France
designer

Cardinale, Claudia
Vides Piazza
Pitagora 9
Rome, Italy
actress

Carew, Rod
2000 State College Blvd.
Anaheim, CA 92806
baseball player

Carey, Hugh L.
Office of the Governor
State Capitol
Albany, NY 12224
governor of New York

Carlin, George
c/o Athena Artists
9100 Wilshire Blvd. #460
Beverly Hills, CA 90212
comedian

Carlin, John
Office of the Governor
Topeka, KS 66612
governor of Kansas

Carlisle, Kitty
32 E. 64th St.
New York, NY 10021
entertainer

Carlos, Juan
Madrid, Spain
king of Spain

Carmichael, Hoagy
1257½ Devon Ave.
Los Angeles, CA 90024
composer

Carnation Co.
5045 Wilshire Blvd.
Los Angeles, CA 90036
H.E. Anderson, president

Carne, Judy
c/o Ruth Webb
9229 Sunset Blvd. #204
Los Angeles, CA 90069
comedienne

Carney, Art
c/o ICM
8899 Beverly Blvd.
Los Angeles, CA 90048
actor

Caron, Leslie
c/o Kohner-Levy Agency
9169 Sunset Blvd.
Los Angeles, CA 90069
actress

Carpenter, Liz
1525 M St. NW #602
Washington DC 20005
co-chairperson, ERAmerica

**Carpenter, Richard
& Karen**
c/o A & M Records
1416 La Brea Ave.
Los Angeles, CA 90028
singers

Carr, Allan
P.O. Box 69670
Los Angeles, CA 90069
producer

Carr, Gerald P.
c/o Bovay Engineers Inc.
P.O. Box 8098
Houston, TX 77004
former astronaut

Carr, Vikki
c/o Regency Artists
9200 Sunset Blvd. # 823
Los Angeles, CA 90069
singer

Carradine, David
c/o Wm. Morris
151 El Camino Drive
Beverly Hills, CA 90212
actor

Carradine, John
c/o Kohner-Levy Agency
9169 Sunset Blvd.
Los Angeles, CA 90069
actor

Carradine, Keith
c/o Ken Fritz Management
8450 Melrose Ave.
Los Angeles, CA 90069
actor

Carrera, Barbara
c/o Chasin-Park-Citron
9255 Sunset Blvd.
Los Angeles, CA 90069
actress

Carroll, Diahann
2660 Benedict Canyon
Beverly Hills, CA 90210
singer

Carroll, Vinette
26 W. 20th St.
New York, Ny 10011
playwright

Carrington, Frank
State National Bank Plaza
1603 Orrington Ave.
Evanston, IL 60201
*director, Americans for
Effective Law Enforcement
Organization*

Cars
c/o Elektra/Asylum Records
962 N. La Cienega Blvd.
Los Angeles, CA 90069
music group

Carson, Johnny
c/o NBC TV
3000 W. Alameda Ave.
Burbank, CA 91505
entertainer

Carswell, G. Harrold
P.O. Box 3833
Tallahassee, FL 32303
*unsuccessful nominee for
U.S. Supreme Court*

Carte Blanche Co.
3460 Wilshire Blvd.
Los Angeles, CA 90010
James Kerr, president

Carter, Amy
The White House
Washington DC 20500
daughter of President Carter

Carter, Billy
P.O. Box 278
Plains, GA 31780
brother of President Carter

Carter, Hodding
2201 C St. NW
Washington DC 20520
*spokesperson for State
Department*

Carter, Jimmy
The White House
Washington DC 20500
president of the United States

Carter, Lillian
Plains, GA 31780
mother of President Carter

Carter, Lynda
c/o Ron Samuels
280 S. Beverly Drive #309
Beverly Hills, CA 90212
actress

Carter, Rosalynn
The White House
Washington DC 20500
wife of President Carter

Carter, Rubin "Hurricane"
Trenton State Prison
Trenton, NJ 08625
convict, former boxer

Cartier Jewelry Co.
653 5th Ave.
New York, NY 10022
Ralph Destino, president

Cartland, Barbara
Camfield Place
Hartfield, Hertfordshire
England
*bestselling author of
romantic fiction*

**Carvel Ice Cream
Company**
201 Saw Mill River Road
Yonkers, NY 10701
Tom Carvel, president

Casals, Rosemary
c/o Women in Tennis
9945 Young Drive
Beverly Hills, CA 90212
tennis player

Casey, Warren
c/o ICM
40 W. 57th St.
New York, NY 10019
playwright

Cash, Johnny
House of Cash
Nashville Pike
Nashville, TN 37075
singer

Cash, June Carter
House of Cash
Nashville Pike
Nashville, TN 37075
singer

Cash, Rosalind
c/o John Sekura
1133 N. Vista St.
Los Angeles, CA 90046
actress

Cassavetes, John
c/o Esme Chandee
9056 Santa Monica Blvd.
#201
Los Angeles, CA 90069
actor

Cassidy, David
c/o Ingels Company
7560 Hollywood Blvd.
Hollywood, CA 90028
actor, singer

Cassidy, Shaun
c/o Wm. Morris
151 El Camino Drive
Beverly Hills, CA 90212
singer, actor

Cassini, Oleg
445 Park Ave.
New York, NY 10022
designer

Castellano, Richard
c/o Douglas S. Cramer & Co.
Colgems Square
Burbank, CA 91505
actor

Castle & Cooke Co.
130 Merchand St.
Honolulu, HI 96813
*Malcolm MacNaughton,
president*

Castro, Fidel
Office of the Premier
Havana, Cuba
premier of Cuba

Cauthen, Steve
c/o International
Management
767 5th Ave.
New York, NY 10022
jockey

Cavett, Dick
c/o Daphne Productions
1790 Broadway
New York, NY 10019
entertainer

Cernan, Eugene A.
c/o Coral Petroleum Inc.
#600
908 Towne Country Blvd.
Houston, TX 77024
former astronaut

Chafee, John H.
Senate Office Building
Washington DC 20510
senator from Rhode Island

Chaffee, Suzy
c/o HT Management
9350 Wilshire Blvd.
Suite 201
Beverly Hills, CA 90212
skier

Chagall, Marc
Vence Alpes Maritimes
France
artist

Chakiris, George
c/o ICM
8899 Beverly Blvd.
Los Angeles, CA 90048
actor

Chamberlain, Richard
c/o Wm. Morris
151 El Camino Drive
Beverly Hills, CA 90212
actor

Chamberlain, Wilt
c/o W.C. Productions
Seymour S. Goldberg
16633 Ventura Blvd.
Encino, CA 91316
retired basketball player

Chambers, Marilyn
c/o Dryden-MacArthur-
Randall
6430 Sunset Blvd. #619
Hollywood, CA 90028
actress

Champion Spark Plug Company
900 Upton Ave.
Toledo, OH 43661
*R.A. Stranahan, Jr.,
president*

Champlin, Charles
c/o *Los Angeles Times*
Times-Mirror Square
Los Angeles, CA 90053
film critic

Chancellor, John
c/o NBC TV
30 Rockefeller Plaza
New York, NY 10020
journalist

Chandler, Dorothy
455 S. Lorraine Blvd.
Los Angeles, CA 90021
*president, Board of Governors—Performing Arts
Council of Los Angeles
Music Center*

Chandler, Otis
Times-Mirror Square
Los Angeles, CA 90053
*publisher, Los Angeles
Times*

Chang, Dr. C.H.
Columbia-Presbyterian
Hospital
622 W. 168th St.
New York, NY 10032
chemotherapy specialist

Channing, Carol
c/o Wm. Morris
151 El Camino Drive
Beverly Hills, CA 90212
actress

Channing, Stockard
c/o Creative Artists Agency
1888 Century Park E.
Suite 1400
Los Angeles, CA 90067
actress

Chapin, Dwight L.
Success Unlimited Magazine
Chicago, IL 60690
*Nixon appointments
secretary*

Chapin, Harry
44 Glen-na-Little Trail
Huntington, NY 11743
singer, songwriter

Chaplin, Geraldine
c/o Charter Management
9000 Sunset Blvd. #1172
Los Angeles, CA 90069
actress

Chaput, Chris
c/o Bill Riordan
1115 Riverside
Salisbury, MD 21801
*skateboarding expert/
teacher*

Charisse, Cyd
c/o MGM Studios
10202 Washington Blvd.
Culver City, CA 90230
dancer

Charles, Prince
Royal Palace
London, England
prince of Wales

Charles, Ray
c/o RPM International Inc.
2107 Washington Blvd.
Los Angeles, CA 90018
singer

Charo
c/o Wm. Morris
151 El Camino Drive
Beverly Hills, CA 90212
entertainer

Chartoff, Robert
c/o MGM Studios
10202 Washington Blvd.
Culver City, CA 90230
film producer

Chase, Chevy
c/o Wm. Morris
151 El Camino Drive
Beverly Hills, CA 90212
comedian

Chasen, Maude
9039 Beverly Blvd.
Los Angeles, CA 90048
restaurateur

Chaudhry, Fazal Elahi
Office of the President
Islambad, Pakistan
president of Pakistan

Chavez, Cesar
c/o AFL-CIO
P.O. Box 62
Keene, CA 93531
labor leader

Chayefsky, Paddy
850 7th Ave.
New York, NY 10019
writer

Cheap Trick
c/o Epic Records
1801 Century Park W.
Los Angeles, CA 90067
music group

Checker, Chubby
c/o Richard Fulton Inc.
850 7th Ave.
New York, NY 10019
singer

Cher
c/o Katz-Gallin-Morey
9255 Sunset Blvd.
Los Angeles, CA 90069
singer

Chertok, Jack
1040 N. Las Palmas St.
Hollywood, CA 90038
producer

Chesimard, Joanne
Yardville Youth
Correctional Center
Yardville, NJ 08620
political activist

Chevron Oil Co.
575 Market St.
San Francisco, CA 94105
D.L. Bower, president

Chicago
c/o Jeff Wald Associates
9356 Santa Monica Blvd.
Beverly Hills, CA 90210
music group

Child, Julia
c/o WGBH TV
125 Western Ave.
Boston, MA 02134
culinary expert

Chiles, Lawton M. Jr.
Senate Office Building
Washington DC 20510
senator from Florida

Ching-huo, Chiang
Taipei, Taiwan
president of Taiwan

Chisolm, Shirley
Congress
Washington DC 20515
U.S. representative

Cho, Emily
663 5th Ave.
New York, NY 10022
shopping consultant

Chock Full O' Nuts Company
425 Lexington Ave.
New York, NY 10017
William Black, president

Christian Science Publishing Society
1 Norway St.
Boston, MA 02115
Frederic Owen, president

Christie, Julie
c/o ICM
8899 Beverly Blvd.
Los Angeles, CA 90048
actress

Chrysler Corporation
12000 Lynn Townsend Drive
Highland Park, MI 48288
Lee Iacocca, president

Church, Frank
Senate Office Bldg.
Washington DC 20510
senator from Idaho

Citizens' Committee for the Right to Bear Arms
1601 114th St. SE
Suite 151
Bellevue, WA 98004
Alan Gottlieb, director

Civil Service Commission
1900 E St. NW
Washington DC 20415
Alan K. Campbell, chairman

Civiletti, Benjamin R.
Justice Department
Constitution Ave. between
9th & 10th Sts.
Washington DC 20530
U.S. attorney general

Clairol Inc.
345 Park Ave.
New York, NY 10022
Lawrence Gelb, president

Clapton, Eric
c/o The Robert Stigwood
Organization
1775 Broadway
New York, NY 10019
musician

Clark, Dick
3003 W. Olive Ave.
Burbank, CA 91505
entertainer, producer

Clark, Joe
Leader of the Opposition
House of Commons
Parliament Building
Ottawa, Canada K1A 1E6
former prime minister

Clark, Petula
c/o NHD International
Service
P.O. Box 498
Quakertown, PA 18951
singer

Clark, Ramsey
37 W. 12th St.
New York, NY 10011
former U.S. attorney general

Classic Cars of America
P.O. Box 443
Madison, NJ 07940
Francis Mulderry, president

Claus, Santa
Santa's House
North Pole
humanitarian

Clayburgh, Jill
c/o Wm. Morris
151 El Camino Drive
Beverly Hills, CA 90212
actress

Cleary, Beverly
c/o Wm. Morrow
105 Madison Ave.
New York, NY 10016
author

Cleaver, Eldridge
c/o Harry Walker Inc.
350 5th Ave.
New York, NY 10001
political activist, author

Cleland, Max
Veteran's Administration
810 Vermont Ave.
Washington DC 20420
veterans' affairs administrator

Clements, Bill
Office of the Governor
Austin, TX 78711
governor of Texas

Clements, William
Sedco Corporation
1901 N. Akard
Dallas, TX 75201
former deputy secretary of defense

Clifford, Clark M.
815 Connecticut Ave.
Washington DC 20006
attorney

Clinton, Bill
Office of the Governor
Little Rock, AR 72201
governor of Arkansas

Clorox Co.
1221 Broadway
Oakland, CA 94612
Robert Shetterly, president

Clough, Susan
The White House
Washington DC 20500
Jimmy Carter's secretary

Clowns of America
717 Beverly Road
Baltimore, MD 21222
Albert E. Sikorsky Jr., editor

Coatsworth, Elizabeth
Chimney Farm
Nobleboro, ME 04555
author

Coburn, James
c/o ICM
8899 Beverly Blvd.
Los Angeles, CA 90048
actor

Coca-Cola Co.
310 North Ave. NW
Atlanta, GA 30313
J. Paul Austin, president

Coca, Imogene
c/o Contemporary-Korman
Artists
132 Lasky Drive
Beverly Hills, CA 90212
comedienne

Cochran, Thad
Senate Office Building
Washington DC 20510
senator from Mississippi

Cody, Iron Eyes
c/o Dade/Rosen Associates
999 N. Doheny Drive
#102
Los Angeles, CA 90069
actor

Coe, Sebastian
Loughborough University
Sheffield, England
world champion runner

Coffin, William Sloane Jr.
Riverside Church
Riverside Drive & 122nd St.
New York, NY 10027
anti-war activist; delivered Christmas services to hostages in Iran

Cohen, Alexander
Shubert Theatre
225 W. 44th St.
New York, NY 10036
producer

Cohen, David
2030 M St. NW
Washington DC 20036
president, Common Cause

Cohen, Willam
Senate Office Building
Washington DC 20510
senator from Maine

Cohn, Roy M.
39 E. 68th St.
New York, NY 10021
attorney

Colbert, Claudette
Bellerive Wt. Peter
Barbabos, West Indies
actress

Colby, William E.
Colby, Miller & Hanes
1625 I St. NW
Washington DC 20006
former CIA director

Cole, Dennis
c/o Robert Raison
Associates
9575 Lime Orchard Road
Beverly Hills, CA 90210
actor

Cole, Gary
919 N. Michigan Ave.
Chicago, IL 60611
photography editor of Playboy

Cole, Natalie
9255 Sunset Blvd. #302
Los Angeles, CA 90069
singer

Coleman, Cy
161 W. 54th St.
New York, NY 10023
composer

Coleman, Gary
c/o William Cunningham
Agency
261 S. Robertson Blvd.
Beverly Hills, CA 90211
actor

Coleman, Dr. James S.
University of Chicago
Chicago, IL 60637
desegregation expert

Coley, John Ford
6436 Sunset Blvd. #1531
Los Angeles, CA 90069
musician, singer

Colgate-Palmolive Co.
300 Park Ave.
New York, NY 10022
D.R. Foster, president

Collin, Frank
2519 W. 71st St.
Chicago, IL 60629
leader, American Nazi Party

Collins, Judy
c/o Rocky Mountain
Productions
1775 Broadway
New York, NY 10019
singer, composer

Collins, Michael
National Air & Space
Museum
Smithsonian Institution
Independence Ave. at 7th
St. SW
Washington DC 20560
former astronaut, museum director

Collins, Dr. W.
Yale University
206 Elm St.
New Haven, CT 06520
neurosurgeon specializing in pituitary tumors & spinal injury

Colson, Charles
1350 Ballantrae Lane
McLean, VA 22101
attorney, convicted Watergate figure

Columbia Broadcasting System
51 W. 52nd St.
New York, NY 10019
William Paley, chairman

Comaneci, Nadia
Gheorge Gheorghiu-Dej
Romania
gymnast

Comfort, Alex
Institute for Higher Comfort
2311 Garden St.
Santa Barbara, CA 93105
author

Commodity Futures Trading Commission
Washington DC 20581
William T. Bagley, chairman

Commodores
c/o Motown Records
6464 Sunset Blvd.
Hollywood, CA 90028
music group

Como, Perry
c/o Roncom MSC
305 Northern Blvd. #3A
Great Neck, NY 11021
singer

Conaway, Jeff
c/o ABC TV
4151 Prospect Ave.
Los Angeles, CA 90027
actor

Condry, James
Dimmit County Chamber of
Commerce
307 N. 5th St.
Carrizo Springs, TX 78834
slingshot champion

Connally, John Bowden Jr.
First National City Bank
Houston, TX 77002
attorney, former governor, presidential candidate

Conniff, Ray
17100 Ventura Blvd.
Encino, CA 91316
conductor

Connors, Chuck
c/o Jay Bernstein
9110 Sunset Blvd.
Los Angeles, CA 90069
actor

Connors, Jimmy
Gerald Lane
Belleville, IL 60507
tennis player

Connors, Mike
c/o Agency for the Performing Arts
9000 Sunset Blvd. #315
Los Angeles, CA 90069
actor

Conrad, Charles Jr.
75 Mead Lane
Englewood, CO 80110
former astronaut

Conrad, Paul
c/o *Los Angeles Times*
Times-Mirror Square
Los Angeles, CA 90053
political cartoonist

Conrad, Robert
c/o David Shapira & Associates
9171 Wilshire Blvd.
Beverly Hills, CA 90210
actor

Conrad, William
c/o Creative Artists Agency
1888 Century Park E.
Suite 1400
Los Angeles, CA 90067
actor

Consolidated Edison Co. of New York
4 Irving Place
New York, NY 10003
Charles F. Luce, president

Constantine, Michael
c/o The Artists Agency
190 N. Canon Drive
Beverly Hills, CA 90210
actor

Continental Airlines
Los Angeles International Airport
Los Angeles, CA 90006
Robert F. Six, president

Convy, Bert
9300 Wilshire Blvd. #501
Beverly Hills, CA 90212
entertainer

Conway, Tim
c/o Weetman
425 S. Beverly Drive
Beverly Hills, CA 90212
comedian

Coogan, Jackie
c/o Kitty Davis
P.O. Box 1305
Hollywood, CA 90028
actor

Cooke, Alistair
1150 5th Ave.
New York, NY 10028
author

Cooke, Terence J.
1011 1st Ave.
New York, NY 10022
cardinal

Cooley, Dr. D.
Texas Heart Institute
Houston, TX 99030
heart surgeon

Coolidge, Rita
c/o Bert Block Management
11 Bailey Ave.
Ridgefield, CT 06877
singer

Cooper, Alice
c/o Alive Enterprises
8530 Wilshire Blvd. #306
Beverly Hills, CA 90211
singer, composer

Cooper, D.
2511 Myers Ave.
Dunbar, WV 25064
organizer of wildwater races

Cooper, Jackie
c/o Wm. Morris
151 El Camino Drive
Beverly Hills, CA 90212
actor, director, producer

Coors, William
Adolph Coors Co.
Golden, CO 80501
chairman of the board

Copland, Aaron
c/o Boosey & Hawkes Inc.
30 W. 57th St.
New York, NY 10019
composer

Coppola, Francis Ford
c/o American Zoetrope Corp.
529 Pacific
San Francisco, CA 94133
film director, producer, writer

Corea, Chick
33 Abbott Ave.
Everett, MA 02149
composer, musician

Cornfeld, Bernie
1100 Carolyn Way
Beverly Hills, CA 90210
financier

Corona, Juan
Vacaville State Prison
Vacaville, CA 95688
convicted mass murderer

Corrigan, Mairead
Peace House
224 Lisburn Road
Belfast 9, Northern Ireland
peace activist

Corso, Gregory
c/o New Productions
330 Avenue of the Americas
New York, NY 10014
writer

Cosby, Bill
c/o Jemmin Inc.
1900 Avenue of the Stars
#1900
Los Angeles, CA 90067
entertainer, actor

Cosell, Howard
c/o ABC TV
1330 Avenue of the Americas
New York, NY 10019
sportscaster

Cossiga, Francesco
Chamber of Deputies
Rome, Italy
premier of Italy

Costanza, Margaret (Midge)
19C Seneca Manor Drive
Rochester, NY 14621
former assistant to Jimmy Carter

Costello, Elvis
c/o Columbia Records
1801 Century Park W.
Los Angeles, CA 90067
singer

Cothran, George
c/o George Cothran Flowers
238 E. 60th St.
New York, NY 10021
floral designer and teacher

Cotten, Joseph
8787 Shoreham Drive
Los Angeles, CA 90069
actor

Cousins, Norman
c/o UCLA Medical School
405 Hilgard Ave.
West Los Angeles, CA 90024
author, editor

Cousteau, Jacques
Musee Oceanografique
Saint Martin, Monaco
oceanographer

Cox, Archibald
Harvard Law School
Cambridge, MA 02138
attorney, Watergate special prosecutor

Cox, Edward Finch
c/o Cravath, Swaine & Moore
1 Chase Manhatten Plaza
New York, NY 10033
husband of Tricia Nixon Cox

Cox, Tricia Nixon
Adams Tower
351 E. 84th St.
New York, NY 10028
daughter of former president

Crabbe, Buster
c/o Cascade Industries Inc.
Talmadge Road
Edison, NJ 08817
actor

Crane, Phillip M.
Congress
Washington DC 20515
*U.S. representative,
presidential candidate*

Cranston, Alan
Senate Office Building
Washington, DC 20510
senator from California

Crawford, Broderick
c/o Contemporary-Korman
Artists Ltd.
132 Lasky Drive
Beverly Hills, CA 90212
actor

Crawford, Christina
c/o Wm. Morrow Co.
105 Madison Ave.
New York, NY 10016
author

Crenna, Richard
c/o Wm. Morris
151 El Camino Drive
Beverly Hills, CA 90212
actor

Crichton, John
9200 Sunset Blvd. # 1000
Los Angeles, CA 90069
author

Crist, Judith
180 Riverside Drive
New York, NY 10024
critic

Crofts, Dash
c/o Day 5 Productions
216 Chatsworth Drive
San Fernando, CA 91340
singer, songwriter

Cronin, Joe
77 Lake Ave.
Newton Centre, MA 02159
*member of baseball
Hall of Fame*

Cronkite, Walter
c/o CBS TV
524 W. 57th St.
New York, NY 10019
journalist

Cronyn, Hume
Box 85 A
Pound Ridge, NY 10576
writer

Crosby, David
c/o ICM
8899 Beverly Blvd.
Los Angeles, CA 90048
musician

Crosby, Kathryn
170 N. Robertson Blvd.
Beverly Hills, CA 90211
actress

Crothers, Scatman
13521 Crewe St.
Van Nuys, CA 91406
entertainer

Crystal, Billy
c/o ABC TV
4151 Prospect Ave.
Los Angeles, CA 90027
actor

Cugat, Xavier
848 N. La Cienega Blvd.
Los Angeles, CA 90069
conductor

Cullen, Bill
530 5th Ave.
New York, NY 10022
entertainer

Culp, Robert
c/o Wm. Morris
151 El Camino Drive
Beverly Hills, CA 90212
actor

Culver, John C.
Senate Office Building
Washington DC 20510
senator from Iowa

Cummings, Quinn
c/o ABC TV
4151 Prospect Ave.
Los Angeles, CA 90027
actress

Curb, Mike
Office of the Lt. Governor
Sacramento, CA 95814
*lt. governor of California,
former record company
executive*

Curie, Eve
1 Sutton Place S.
New York, NY 10022
daughter of Marie Curie

Curreri, Dr. P.W.
N.Y. Hospital
Cornell Medical Center
1300 York Ave.
New York, NY 10021
*burn specialist - pediatric
and adult*

Curtin, Jane
c/o NBC TV
30 Rockefeller Plaza
New York, NY 10020
comedienne

Curtis, Ken
c/o Warren Wever
Management
1104 S. Robertson Blvd.
Los Angeles, CA 90035
actor

Curtis, Tony
c/o Irving Lazar
211 S. Beverly Drive
Beverly Hills, CA 90212
actor, author

Dahl, Arlene
Dahli Enterprises Ltd.
730 5th Ave.
New York, NY 10019
actress, author

Dahl, Roald
Gipsy House
Great Missenden Bucks
England
author

Dali, Salvador
c/o Carstairs Gallery
11 E. 57th St.
New York, NY 10022
artist

Dallas Cowboy Cheerleaders
6116 N. Central Expressway
Dallas, TX 75206
precision dance/cheer team

Dalton, John N.
Office of the Governor
Richmond, VA 23219
governor of Virginia

Damone, Vic
c/o Wm. Morris
151 El Camino Drive
Beverly Hills, CA 90212
singer

Dana, Bill
c/o Shapiro/West Associates
141 El Camino Drive
Suite 205
Beverly Hills, CA 90212
entertainer

Danforth, John C.
Senate Office Building
Washington DC 20510
senator from Missouri

Dangerfield, Rodney
1118 1st Ave.
New York, NY 10022
comedian

Daniel, Margaret Truman
c/o *New York Times*
229 W. 43rd St.
New York, NY 10023
author, daughter of late president

Dannay, Frederick
29 Byron Lane
Larchmont, NY 10538
mystery writer, co-author under pseudonym "Ellery Queen"

Dante, Nicholas
250 W. 75th St.
New York, NY 10023
playwright

Danza, Tony
c/o ABC TV
4151 Prospect Ave.
Hollywood, CA 90027
actor

Darvick, Herman M.
P.O. Box 467
Rockville Centre, NY 11571
president, Universal Autograph Collectors Club

Das Gupta, Dr. T.K.
University of Illinois
Chicago, IL 60612
surgeon specializing in melanoma

Dash, Samuel
Georgetown University Law Center
Washington DC 20001
counsel to Watergate Committee

David, Hal
Elm Drive
East Hills
Roslyn, NY 11576
lyricist

Davidson, John
c/o 20th Century Records
8255 Sunset Blvd.
Los Angeles, CA 90046
entertainer

Davidson, Ralph
c/o Time, Inc.
Time-Life Building
Rockefeller Center
New York, NY 10020
publisher

Davidson, Raymond
300 E. 33rd St. Apt. 1G
New York, NY 10016
cartoonist

Davies, Peter Maxwell
c/o Boosey & Hawkes
295 Regent St.
London, WIR 8JH
England
composer

Davis, Angela U.
c/o Random House
201 E. 50th St.
New York, NY 10022
political activist

Davis, Bette
River Road
Weston, CT 06883
actress

Davis, Ed
Los Angeles Police Dept.
Los Angeles, CA 90070
*former Los Angeles chief
of police*

Davis, Mac
c/o Katz-Gallin-Morey
Enterprises
9255 Sunset Blvd.
Suite 1115
Los Angeles, CA 90069
entertainer

Davis, Miles
c/o Neil Reshin
54 Main St.
Danbury, CT 06810
trumpet player, composer

Davis, Rennie
Birth of a New Nation, Inc.
905 S. Gilpin
Denver, CO 80209
Chicago Seven defendant

Davis, Sammy Jr.
c/o Syni Corp.
2029 Century Park E.
Los Angeles, CA 90067
entertainer

Dawber, Pam
c/o ABC TV
4151 Prospect Ave.
Los Angeles, CA 90027
actress

Dawson, Richard
c/o ABC TV
1330 Avenue of the Americas
New York, NY 10019
entertainer

Day, Doris
c/o Wm. Morris
151 El Camino Drive
Beverly Hills, CA 90212
actress, singer

Dean, John W. III
c/o David Obst
105 E. 64th St.
New York, NY 10021
*attorney, former White
House counsel*

DeBakey, Michael
5323 Cherokee St.
Houston, TX 77005
surgeon

**Debecker, Luc Jean-
Francois**
5 B Chemic Golette
1217 Meyrin
Geneve, Switzerland
*surveyor who discovered
ancient cave paintings*

DeBell, Kristine
c/o Sharon Kemp
8601 Wilshire Blvd.
Suite 601
Beverly Hills, CA 90211
actress, model

**de Butts, Robert
E. Lee.**
402 Virginia Ave.
Alexandria, VA 22303
*great-grandson of Gen.
Robert E. Lee and great-
great-great-great-grandson
of Martha Custis Washington
wife of George Washington*

deCarlo, Yvonne
3160 Coldwater Canyon
N. Hollywood, CA 91604
actress

DeCarteret, Percy
Visalia, CA 93277
*America's oldest flight
instructor (84 years old)*

DeConcini, Dennis
Senate Office Building
Washington DC 20510
senator from Arizona

Dee, Kiki
c/o John Reid Enterprises
211 S. Beverly Drive #200
Beverly Hills, CA 90212
singer

Dee, Sandra
c/o David Gershenson
9441 Wilshire Blvd. # 620 A
Los Angeles, CA 90212
actress

De Franco, Buddy
c/o Maximus Agency Corp
39 W. 55th St.
New York, NY 10019
clarinetist

De Givenchy, Hubert
Givenchy
3 Ave. George V
75008 Paris, France
designer

De Havilland, Olivia
75764 Paris Cedex 16
France
actress

Delamare, George
6 Ave. General Leclerc
Borte Postale 59
54500 Vandoeuvre
France
medical student developing techniques allowing paraplegics to walk

Delamo, Mario
316 E. 63rd St.
New York, NY 10021
dancer

Delco Car Parts Co.
P.O. Box 1042
Dayton, OH 45401
W.B. Thompson, president

De Laurentiis, Dino
Dino De Laurentiis Corp.
202 N. Canon Drive
Beverly Hills, CA 90210
film producer

Della Femina, Jerry
535 Madison Ave.
New York, NY 10022
advertising executive, author

Del Rio, Dolores
c/o Fernando Alencaster
96 Mexico 10, D.F.
actress

Delta Air Lines
Hartsfield Atlanta
International Airport
Atlanta, GA 30320
W.T. Beebe, president

De Luise, Dom
c/o Howard Rothberg
116 N. Robertson Blvd. #901
Los Angeles, CA 90048
actor

Demento, Dr.
c/o Larry Gordon
6671 Sunset Blvd. #1591
Los Angeles, CA 90028
disc jockey

deMoss Wolfe, Glynn
Blythe, CA 92225
world's most married man (22 times)

Deneuve, Catherine
c/o Artmedia
10 Ave. George V
75008 Paris, France
actress

De Niro, Robert
c/o Ufland Agency
190 N. Canon Drive
Beverly Hills, CA 90210
actor

Dennis, Sandy
Cranberry Road
Weston, CT 06883
actress

Dent, Harry S.
485 L'Enfant Plaza W. SW
Washington DC 20010
Nixon campaign strategist

Denton, Harold
Nuclear Regulatory
Commission
Washington DC 20555
nuclear reactor regulation director

Denver, John
P.O. Box 1567
Aspen, CO 81611
singer, songwriter, actor

Derby, Ethel
Safamore Hill
Oyster Bay, NY 11771
daughter of Theodore Roosevelt

Derek, Bo
c/o Martin Baum
1888 Century Park E.
Suite 1400
Los Angeles, CA 90067
actress

Dern, Bruce
c/o Wm. Morris
151 El Camino Drive
Beverly Hills, CA 90212
actor

d'Estaing, Valery Giscard
Paris, France
president of France

Devane, William
c/o Wm. Morris
151 El Camino Drive
Beverly Hills, CA 90212
actor

De Vito, Danny
c/o Paramount TV
5451 Marathon St.
Hollywood, CA 90038
actor

Devo
c/o Warner Brothers Records
3300 Warner Blvd.
Burbank, CA 91522
music group

DeWitt, Joyce
c/o Goldberg-Ehrlich
9701 Wilshire Blvd. #800
Beverly Hills, CA 90212
actress

DeWitt, Lew
P.O. Box 2703
Staunton, VA 24401
songwriter

Diamond, Neil
c/o Management III
9744 Wilshire Blvd.
Beverly Hills, CA 90212
singer, composer

Dickerson, Nancy
c/o Lewis Associates
156 E. 52nd St.
New York, NY 10022
journalist

Dickey, Bill
114 E. 5th St.
Little Rock, AR 85251
*member of baseball Hall
of Fame*

Dickinson, Angie
c/o The Blake Agency Ltd.
409 N. Camden Drive
Beverly Hills, CA 90210
actress

Diefenbacker, John
115 Lansdowne Road
Ottawa, Ontario
Canada
*former prime minister
of Canada*

Dietrich, Marlene
c/o Regency Artists Ltd.
9200 Sunset Blvd. Suite 823
Los Angeles, CA 90069
actress

Diggs, Charles C. Jr.
Congress
Washington DC 20515
U.S. representative

Diller, Phyllis
c/o Phil Dil Productions Ltd.
One Dag Hammarskjold
Plaza
New York, NY 10017
comedienne

DiMaggio, Joe
2150 Beach St.
San Francisco, CA 94123
*member of baseball Hall
of Fame*

Dinah!
c/o KTLA
5800 Sunset Blvd.
Los Angeles, CA 90028
*Launa Newman, talent
coordinator*

**Diner's Club Credit
Card Company**
10 Columbus Circle
New York, NY 10019
R. Newell Lusby, president

**Di Sant'Angelo,
Giorgio**
20 W. 57th St.
New York, NY 10019
fashion designer

Dixon, Jeanne
c/o James L. Dixon & Co.
1225 Connecticut Ave. NW
Washington DC 20036
psychic, astrologist

Doar, John
30 Rockefeller Plaza
New York, NY 10020
attorney

Doda, Carol
300 Columbus Circle
San Francisco, CA 94133
topless dancer

Dole, Robert J.
Senate Office Building
Washington DC 20510
*senator from Kansas;
presidential candidate*

Domenici, Pete V.
Senate Office Building
Washington DC 20510
senator from New Mexico

Domino, "Fats"
c/o ABC
445 Park Ave.
New York, NY 10022
musician

Donahue, Elinor
c/o Diamond Artists
9200 Sunset Blvd.
Los Angeles, CA 90069
actress

Donahue, Phil
c/o WGN TV
2501 Bradley Place
Chicago, IL 60618
talk show host

Donovon (Leitch)
c/o Magna Artists
1370 Avenue of the Americas
New York, NY 10019
singer, composer

Doobie Brothers
c/o Warner Brothers Records
3300 Warner Blvd.
Burbank, CA 91510
music group

Doubleday, Nelson
245 Park Ave.
New York, NY 10017
publisher

Douglas, Kirk
c/o Wm. Morris
151 El Camino Drive
Beverly Hills, CA 90212
actor

Douglas, Melvyn
50 Riverside Drive
New York, NY 10024
actor

Douglas, Michael
c/o Wm. Morris
151 El Camino Drive
Beverly Hills, CA 90212
actor, director

Douglas, Mike
c/o CBS TV
7800 Beverly Blvd.
Los Angeles, CA 90036
talk show host

Mike Douglas Show
7800 Beverly Blvd.
Hollywood, CA 90036
Vince Calandra, talent coordinator

Dow Chemical Co.
2030 Dow Center
Midland, MI 48640
C.B. Branch, president

Dow Jones Co.
22 Cortland St.
New York, NY 10007
William Kirby, president

Dowd, Timothy
Deputy Police Chief
New York City Police Dept.
One Police Plaza
New York, NY 10038
headed search for "Son of Sam"

Downs, Hugh
P.O. Box 1132
Carefree, AZ 85331
journalist

Doyle Dane Bernbach Advertising
437 Madison Ave.
New York, NY 10022
William Bernbach, president

Doyle, David
9454 Wilshire Blvd. #302
Beverly Hills, CA 90212
actor

Dreyfus, Lee S.
Office of the Governor
Madison, WI 53702
governor of Wisconsin

Dreyfus Mutual Fund Company
767 5th Ave.
New York, NY 10022
Howard Stein, president

Dreyfuss, Richard
P.O. Box 5367
Santa Monica, CA 90405
actor

Drury, Allen
c/o Doubleday & Co.
245 Park Ave.
New York, NY 10017
author

Dubos, Dr. Rene
Rockefeller University
1230 York Ave.
New York, NY 10021
bacteriologist

Duchin, Peter
Peter Duchin Orchestras
400 Madison Ave.
New York, NY 10017
pianist

Duck, Donald
c/o Walt Disney Productions
500 S. Buena Vista St.
Burbank, CA 91521
cartoon character

Duffey, Joseph D.
806 15th St. NW
Washington DC 20005
chairman, National Endowment for the Humanities

Duffy, Patrick
c/o CBS TV
7800 Beverly Blvd.
Los Angeles, CA 90036
actor

Duke Astin, Patty
c/o Creative Artists Agency
1888 Century Park E. #1400
Los Angeles, CA 90067
actress

Dun & Bradstreet
299 Park Ave.
New York, NY 10017
Harrington Drake, president

Dunaway, Faye
c/o ICM
8899 Beverly Blvd.
Los Angeles, CA 90048
actress

Duncan, Charles
U.S. Department of Energy
Washington DC 20545
secretary of energy

Duncan, Sandy
c/o APA
9000 Sunset Blvd. #315
Los Angeles, CA 90069
actress, dancer

Dunlop, John T.
236 Baker Library
Harvard University
Boston, MA 02163
*economics professor;
former secretary of labor*

Du Pont Company
9000 Du Pont Building
Wilmington, DE 19898
Irving Shapiro, president

Du Pont, Edmond
P.O. Box 507
Wilmington, DE 19899
financier

Du Pont, Pierre S. IV
Office of the Governor
Legislative Hall
Dover, DE 19901
governor of Delaware

Du Pont, Dr. Robert
National Institute on
Drug Abuse
11400 Rockville Pike
Rockville, MD 20852
government official

Durbin, Deanna
Neauph de le Chateau
France
singer, actress

Durenberger, David
Senate Office Building
Washington DC 20510
senator from Minnesota

Durkin, John A.
Senate Office Building
Washington DC 20510
*senator from
New Hampshire*

Durocher, Leo
1400 E. Palm Canyon
Palm Springs, CA 92262
former baseball manager

Duvall, Robert
c/o The Blake Agency
409 N. Camden Drive
Beverly Hills, CA 90210
actor

Dykstra, John
6842 Valjean Ave.
Van Nuys, CA 91406
*motion picture special
effects artist*

Dylan, Bob
P.O. Box 264
Cooper Station, NY 10003
singer, composer

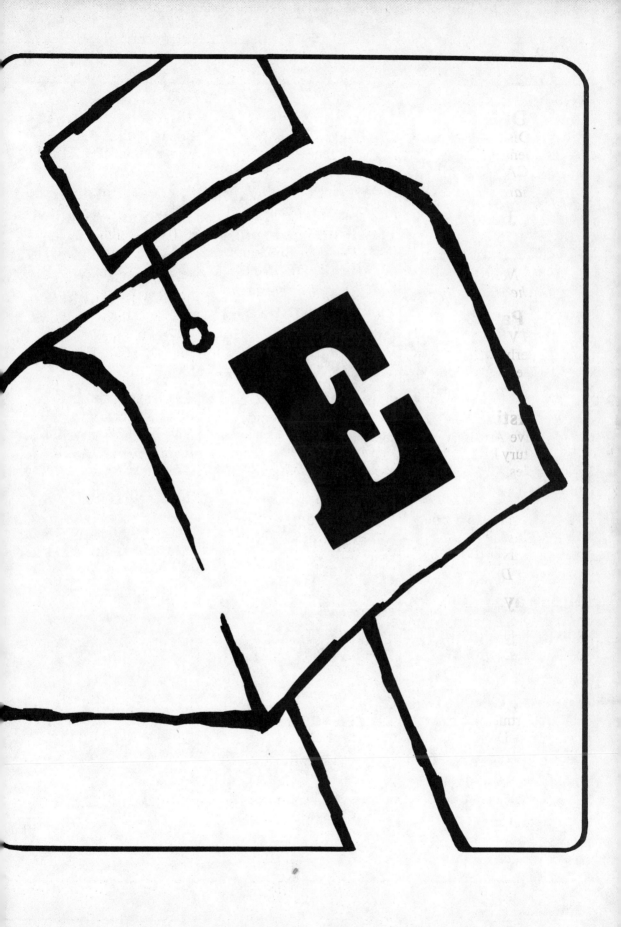

Eagles
3380 Melrose Ave. #307
Los Angeles, CA 90069
music group

Eagleton, Thomas F.
Senate Office Building
Washington DC 20510
senator from Missouri

Earth, Wind & Fire
c/o Cavallo-Ruffalo
9885 Charleville Blvd.
Beverly Hills, CA 90210
music group

Eastern Airlines
Miami International Airport
Miami, FL 33148
Frank Borman, president

Eastwood, Clint
c/o Guttman & Pam
120 El Camino Drive #104
Beverly Hills, CA 90212
actor

Ebensten, Hanns
Hanns Ebensten Travel, Inc.
55 W. 42nd St.
New York, NY 10036
organizes unusual vacations

Ebert, Robert
401 N. Wabash Ave.
Chicago, IL 60611
film critic

Ebsen, Buddy
c/o James McHugh Agency
150 Beverly Blvd. #206
Los Angeles, CA 90048
actor, dancer

Edelin, Dr. Kenneth
720 Harrison Ave. #201
Boston, MA 02118
pro-abortion activist

Eden, Barbara
c/o Hanson & Schwam
9229 Sunset Blvd.
Los Angeles, CA 90069
actress, entertainer

**Edinburgh, H.R.H.
The Prince Philip,
Duke of Edinburgh**
Buckingham Palace
London, S.W.I., England
*prince of the United
Kingdom of Great Britain &
N. Ireland*

Edsel Owner's Club
West Liberty, IL 62475
Perry E. Piper, founder

Edwards, Blake
135 Copley Place
Beverly Hills, CA 90210
director, writer

Edwards, Stephanie
c/o Weisner, Demann
Entertainment
9200 Sunset Blvd.
Penthouse
Los Angeles, CA 90069
entertainer

Eggar, Samantha
c/o Wm. Morris
151 El Camino Drive
Beverly Hills, CA 90212
actress

Ehrlichman, John D.
c/o Simon & Schuster
1230 Avenue of the Americas
New York, NY 10020
*former Nixon aide, convicted
Watergate conspirator*

Eilberg, Joshua
Congress
Washington DC 20515
U.S. representative

Einstein, Elizabeth
1090 Creston Road
Berkeley, CA 94708
*neurochemist;
daughter-in-law of late
Albert Einstein*

Eisenstadt, Samuel
The Hebrew University
Jerusalem, Israel
professor of sociology

**Eisenhower, David
(Dwight D., II)**
David Obst
105 E. 64th St.
New York, NY 10021
grandson of late president

Eisenhower, John
1637 Jones Road
Valley Forge, PA 19481
former ambassador

**Eisenhower, Julie
Nixon**
Capistrano Beach, CA 92624
daughter of former president

Eizenstat, Stuart
The White House
Washington DC 20500
presidental assistant for
domestic affairs and policy

Ekland, Britt
c/o Rush/Flaherty Agency
10889 Wilshire Blvd. #1130
Los Angeles, CA 90024
actress

Electric Light Orchestra
c/o Don & David Arden
44 Park Side
Winbledon, London
England SW19
music group

Elektra Asylum Record Company
962 N. La Cienega Blvd.
Los Angeles, CA 90069
Joe Smith, president

Elizabeth II, Queen (Windsor)
Buckingham Palace
London, England
queen of England

Elliman, Yvonne
c/o The Robert Stigwood
Organization
1775 Broadway
New York, NY 10019
singer

Elliott, Bob
420 Lexington Ave.
New York, NY 10021
comedian (Bob & Ray)

Ellsberg, Daniel
3 Aladdin Terrace
San Francisco, CA 94133
political activist who
disclosed Pentagon Papers

el-Qaddafi, Muammar
Tripoli, Libya
dictator

Ely, Ron
1617 Casale Road
Pacific Palisades, CA 90272
actor

Emerson, Lake & Palmer
c/o Manticore Management
170 E. 61st St.
New York, NY 10021
music group

Emery Air Freight
Wilton, CT 06897
James McNulty, president

Enders, Thomas O.
Embassy of the United States
Ottawa, Ontario
Canada K1P 5T1
ambassador to Canada

Engel, Georgia
7080 Yucca St.
Hollywood, CA 90028
actress

Englert, Kenneth
9095 County Road #120
Salida, CO 81201
organizer of buffalo chip
throwing contest

Environmental Protection Agency
401 M St. SW
Washington DC 20460
Douglas Costle,
administrator

Epstein, William
United Nations Institute for
Training & Research
801 UN Plaza
New York, NY 10017
developing new approaches
for arms control and
disarmament

Erhard, Werner
Erhard Seminars Training
765 California St.
San Francisco, CA 94108
founder of est

Ervin, Sam J. Jr.
P.O. Box 69
Morganton, NC 28655
chairman of the senate
Watergate committee

Erving, Julius "Dr. J"
c/o Philadelphia '76ers
301 City Line Ave.
Bala Cynwyd, PA 19004
basketball player

Estrada, Erik
P.O. Box 2882
Hollywood, CA 90028
actor

Evans, Dale
c/o Art Rush
10221 Riverside Drive
No. Hollywood, CA 91602
singer, author

Evans, John
Holman Prison
Atmore, AL 36502
prisoner on death row

Evans, John V.
Office of the Governor
Boise, ID 83720
governor of Idaho

Evans, Robert
c/o Paramount Pictures Corp.
5451 Marathon St.
Los Angeles, CA 90038
*motion picture studio
executive*

Everett, Chad
c/o Creative Artists Agency
1888 Century Park E.
#1400
Los Angeles, CA 90067
actor

Everroad, Coach Jim
c/o Price/Stern/Sloan
Publishers, Inc.
410 N. La Cienega Blvd.
Los Angeles, CA 90048
author, physical fitness expert

Evers, Charles
City Hall
Fayette, MS 39069
mayor, civil rights activist

Exon, John J. Jr.
Senate Office Building
Washington DC 20510
senator from Nebraska

Exxon Corporation
1251 Avenue of the Americas
New York, NY 10020
C.C. Garvin Jr., president

Faberge
1345 Avenue of the Americas
New York, NY 10019
George Barrie, president

Fabian (Forte)
9221 Charleville Blvd.
Beverly Hills, CA 90212
singer, actor

Fabrares, Shelly
c/o APA
9000 Sunset Blvd.
Los Angeles, CA 90069
actress

Fabray, Nanette
14360 Sunset Blvd.
Pacific Palisades, CA 90272
actress

Fahl, Rudy
2400 West Colorado Ave.
Colorado Springs, CO 80904
organizer of Pike's Peak marathon

Fain, Sammy
1640 San Ysidro Drive
Beverly Hills, CA 90210
composer

Fairbanks, Douglas Jr.
10 Park Place
London SW1 England
actor

Fairmont Hotel
San Francisco, CA 94106
Benjamin Swig, president

Falana, Lola
c/o Wm. Morris
151 El Camino Drive
Beverly Hills, CA 90212
entertainer

Falco, Louis
209 E. 2nd St.
New York, NY 10009
choreographer

Falk, Peter
c/o Wm. Morris
1350 Avenue of the Americas
New York, NY 10019
actor

Family Feud
Goodson-Todman
Productions
6430 Sunset Blvd.
Hollywood, CA 90028
Howard Felsher, talent co-ordinator

Fannin, Paul J.
5990 Orange Blossom Lane
Phoenix, AZ 85018
former senator

Farenthold, Frances T.
Wells College
Aurora, NY 13026
women's rights activist

Fargo, Donna
P.O. Box 15743
Nashville, TN 37215
singer

Farr, Jamie
c/o 20th Century Fox
10201 W. Pico Blvd.
Los Angeles, CA 90064
actor

Farrell, Mike
c/o Acara, Bauman & Hiller
9220 Sunset Blvd. Suite 322
Lo Angeles, CA 90069
actor

Farrow, Mia
c/o Jesse Morgan
6300 Wilshire Blvd.
Los Angeles, CA 90048
actress

Fawcett, Farah
c/o Wm. Morris
151 El Camino Drive
Beverly Hills, CA 90212
actress

Fawcett, Roger
Brush Island Road
Darien, CT 06820
former president, Fawcett Publications

Federal Election Commission
1325 K St. NW
Washington DC 20463
Thomas E. Harris, chairman

Federal Trade Commission
Pennsylvania Ave. at
6th St. NW
Washington DC 20580
Michael Pertschuk, chairman

Feiffer, Jules
60 Riverside Drive
New York, NY 10024
cartoonist

Feinstein Blum, Diane
City Hall
Van Ness Ave.
San Francisco, CA 94102
mayor of San Francisco

Feldman, Marty
c/o 20th Century Fox
10201 W. Pico Blvd.
Los Angeles, CA 90064
comedian

Feliciano, Jose
415 N. Tustin Ave.
Orange, CA 92667
musician

Felker, Clay
322 E. 57th St.
New York, NY 10024
publisher

Fell, Norman
c/o Contemporary-Korman
Artists Ltd.
132 Lasky Drive
Beverly Hills, CA 90212
actor

Feller, Bob
P.O. Box 6057
Cleveland, OH 44101
former baseball player

Fender, Freddy
5626 Brock St.
Houston, TX 77023
singer

Fenwick, Millicent
House Office Building
Washington DC 20515
U.S. representative

Feminist Karate Union
101 Hickerson Suite 250 A
Seattle, WA 98109
Py Bateman, director

Ferlinghetti, Lawrence
City Lights Bookstore
261 Columbus Ave.
San Francisco, CA 94133
poet

Fernanado, Aruna
Steggles Breeding Unit
Wallalong, Via Martland
New South Wales, 2321
Australia
developed cheap and efficient system of getting protein food to the Third World

Ferrer, Jose
c/o MEW Co.
151 N. San Vincente Blvd.
Beverly Hills, CA 90211
actor

Ferrigno, Lou
c/o CBS TV
7800 Beverly Blvd.
Los Angeles, CA 90036
actor

Fidrych, Mark
c/o Detroit Tigers
Tigers Stadium
Detroit, MI 48216
baseball player

Fiedler, Mrs. Arthur
133 Hyslop Road
Brookline, MA 02146
widow of Arthur Fiedler

Field, Sally
c/o Wm. Morris
151 El Camino Drive
Beverly Hills, CA 90212
actress

Finch, Robert Hutchinson
c/o Fleming, Anderson et al.
301 E. Colorado Blvd. #704
Pasadena, CA 91101
attorney

Fingers, Rollie
P.O. Box 2000
San Diego, CA 92120
baseball player

Findley, Charles O.
c/o Oakland As
Oakland-Alameda
County Coliseum
Oakland, CA 94621
baseball executive

Firestone, Raymond
Lauray Farms
Bath, OH 44210
retired tire company executive

Firestone Tire & Rubber Company
1200 Firestone Pkwy.
Akron, OH 44317
Richard Riley, president

Fischer, Bobby
c/o Management III
1345 Avenue of the Americas
New York, NY 10019
chess player

Fisher, Carrie
c/o Chasin-Park-Citron
9255 Sunset Blvd.
Los Angeles, CA 90069
actress

Fisher, Eddie
c/o Wm. Morris
1350 Avenue of the Americas
New York, NY 10019
singer

Fisher, Florence
P.O. Box 154
Washington Bridge Station
New York, NY 10033
founder of Adoptee's Liberty Movement (arranges re-unions between adoptees and natural parents)

Fitzgerald, A. Ernest
The Pentagon
Washington DC 20330
Pentagon cost analyst

Fitzgerald, Ella
c/o Grantz
451 N. Canon Drive
Beverly Hills. CA 90210
singer

Fitzgerald, Geraldine
c/o ICM
40 W. 57th St.
New York, NY 10019
actress

Fitzgerald, Jan
488 Madison Ave.
New York, NY 10022
publisher, US Magazine

Fitzpatrick, Mary
The White House
Washington DC 20500
nurse to Amy Carter; parolee

Fitzsimmons, Frank E.
c/o International
Brotherhood of Teamsters
25 Louisiana Ave. NW
Washington DC 20001
president of Teamster's Union

Flack, Roberta
600 New Hampshire Ave.
NW #430
Washington DC 20037
singer

Flaherty, Peter F.
Deputy Attorney General
U.S. Dept. of Justice
Washington DC 20530
government official

Fleischmann, Isaac
Patent & Trademark Office
Crystal Palace – Room 32 D01
2021 Jefferson Davis Hwy.
Arlington, VA 20231
director, Patent & Trademark Office

Fleetwood Mac
c/o ICM
8899 Beverly Blvd.
Los Angeles, CA 90048
music group

Fleming, Peggy
1626 14th Ave.
San Francisco, CA 94122
figure skater

Fleming, Rhonda
9255 Doheny Drive #1602
Los Angeles, CA 90069
actress

Flemming, Arthur S.
U.S. Commission on
Civil Rights
Washington DC 20425
commission chairman

Fletcher, Dr. G.
M.D. Anderson Hospital &
Tumor Institute
6723 Bertner Drive
Houston, TX 77030
chemotherapy specialist

Fletcher, Louise
c/o Columbia Pictures
711 5th Ave.
New York, NY 10022
actress

Flintstone, Fred
c/o Hanna-Barbera
Productions
3400 Cahuenga Blvd.
Los Angeles, CA 90068
cartoon character

**Flowers, Wayland
(and Madame)**
c/o Patty Lee
6034½ Graciosa Drive
Hollywood, CA 90028
entertainer

Fly Without Fear
101 Park Ave.
New York, NY 10017
Carol Gross, director

Flynt, Larry
c/o Hustler Magazine
2029 Century Park E.
Los Angeles, CA 90067
publisher

Fonda, Albert
c/o Engineers Club
of Philadelphia
1317 Spruce
Philadelphia, PA 19107
*president, American Society
of Inventors*

Fonda, Henry
c/o John Springer Associates
1901 Avenue of the Stars
Los Angeles, CA 90067
actor

Fonda, Jane
c/o Wm. Morris
151 El Camino Drive
Beverly Hills, CA 90212
actress

Fonda, Peter
c/o Film Artists
8278 Sunset Blvd.
Los Angeles, CA 90046
actor

Fong, Hiram L.
195 S. King St.
Honolulu, HI 96817
former senator

Fontaine, Joan
c/o The Gage Group
8732 Sunset Blvd.
Los Angeles, CA 90069
actress

Foote, Emerson
Gipsy Trail
Carmel, CA 10512
retired advertising executive

Forbes, Malcolm
60 5th Ave.
New York, NY 10011
publisher

Ford, Betty
Rancho Mirage, CA 92270
former first lady

Ford, Eileen
344 E. 59th St.
New York, NY 10022
modeling agency executive

**Ford, Ernie
"Tennessee"**
P.O. Box 31-552
San Francisco, CA 94131
entertainer

Ford, Gerald
Rancho Mirage, CA 92270
former president

Ford, Glenn
c/o Wm. Morris
151 El Camino Drive
Beverly Hills, CA 90212
actor

Ford, Henry II
Grosse Pointe Farms,
MI 48236
automobile manufacturer

Ford, Susan
Rancho Mirage, CA 92270
*photographer; daughter of
former president*

Ford, Wendell H.
Senate Office Building
Washington DC 20510
senator from Kentucky

Ford, Whitey
38 Schoolhouse Lane
Lake Success, NY 11020
*member of baseball Hall of
Fame*

Foreman, Carl
1370 Avenue of the Americas
New York, NY 10019
film producer

Foreman, George
c/o Dick Sadler
23900 Madeiras Ave.
Hayward, CA 94541
*former world heavyweight
boxing champion*

Forman, Milos
c/o Robert Lantz
114 E. 55th St.
New York, NY 10022
director

Forsythe, John
11560 Bellagio Road
Los Angeles, CA 90049
actor

Fortas, Abe
1200 29th St. NW
Washington DC 20007
*former Supreme Court
justice*

Fortune Society
29 E. 22nd St.
New York, NY 10010
*David Rothenberg, executive
director (penal reform,
ex-convict aid)*

Fosse, Bob
58 W. 58th St.
New York, NY 10019
producer

Foster, Jodie
c/o Ufland Agency
100 N. Canon Drive
Beverly Hills, CA 90210
actress

Fox, Rodney
Sea & Sea Travel Service,
Inc.
680 Beach St. Suite 340
Wharfside
San Francisco, CA 94109
world's top shark authority

Foxx, Redd
933 La Brea Ave.
Los Angeles, CA 90028
entertainer

Foyt, A.J.
6415 Toledo
Houston, TX 77008
race driver

Frampton, Peter
c/o Bandana Enterprises
595 Madison Ave. #1201
New York, NY 10022
singer

Franciosa, Tony
c/o Creative Artists Agency
1888 Century Park E.
Los Angeles, CA 90067
actor

Francis, Arlene
Ritz Tower
57th & Park Ave.
New York, NY 10021
television personality

Franciscus, James
c/o ICM
8899 Beverly Blvd.
Los Angeles, CA 90048
actor

Frank, J. Howard
P.O. Box 520
Vero Beach, FL 32969
*developer of international
color standard for biology*

Franklin, Aretha
c/o Sackheim Agency
9301 Wilshire Blvd.
Beverly Hills, CA 90210
singer

Franklin, David
9 Preston Road
Somerville, MA 02143
*developing techniques of
hearing through the skin for
the deaf*

Franklin Mint
Franklin Center
Philadelphia, PA 19091
Brian Harrison, president

Frazier, Joe
c/o Coverlay Inc.
Western Savings
Fund Building
Broad & Chestnut Sts.
Philadelphia, PA 19107
*former world heavyweight
boxing champion*

Frazier, Malcolm
Office of the Prime Minister
Canberra, Australia
prime minister of Australia

Frazier, Walt
Walt Frazer Enterprises
370 Lexington Ave.
New York, NY 10017
retired basketball player

Frederick's of Hollywood
6608 Hollywood Blvd.
Hollywood, CA 90028
*Frederick Mellinger,
president*

Friedan, Betty
One Lincoln Plaza
New York, NY 10023
feminist leader

Friedheim, Jerry W.
American Newspaper
Publishers Assn.
11600 Sunrise Road
Reston, VA 22091
manager

Friedman, Daniel M.
U.S. Court of Claims
Washington DC 20005
chief judge

Friedman, Dr. E.
Beth-Israel Hospital
330 Brookline Ave.
Boston, MA 02215
*specialist in high-risk
pregnancy and
abnormal labor*

Friedman, Milton
Hoover Institution
Stanford, CA 94305
economist

Frito-Lay Company
Frito-Lay Tower
Tower Exchange
Dallas, TX 75235
Herman W. Lay, president

**Fromme, Lynette
"Squeaky"**
Federal Reformatory for
Women
Alderson, WV 24910
*would-be assassin of Gerald
Ford*

Frost, David
46 Egerton Crescent
London SW 3 England
producer, talk show host

Fuchs, Dr. F.
New York Hospital
Cornell Medical Center
1300 York Ave.
New York, NY 10021
*specialist in high-risk
pregnancy and abnormal
labor*

**Fulbright, James
William**
815 Connecticut Ave.
Washington DC 20006
attorney, former senator

Fuller Brush Co.
P.O. Box 729
Great Bend, KS 67530
Nat Zivin, president

**Fuller, R.
Buckminster**
Hoover Institution
3500 Market St.
Philadelphia, PA 19104
educator

Funicello, Annette
16102 Sandy Lane
Encino, CA 91316
actress

Funt, Allen
60 W. 55th St.
New York, NY 10019
television host

Furness, Betty
c/o NBC TV
30 Rockefeller Plaza
New York, NY 10020
consumer advocate

Furth, George
3030 Durand Drive
Hollywood, CA 90068
actor, playwright

GAF Company
140 W. 51st St.
New York, NY 10020
Jesse Werner, president

**Gable, Kay
(Mrs. Clark)**
900 N. Roxbury Drive
Beverly Hills, CA 90210
widow of Clark Gable

Gabor, Eva
c/o ICM
8899 Beverly Blvd.
Los Angeles, CA 90048
actress

Gabor, Zsa Zsa
c/o Robert Hussong Agency
9000 Sunset Blvd.
Los Angeles, CA 90069
actress

Gabriel, Roman
Sunrise Country Club
Rancho Mirage, CA 92270
*actor, former
football player*

Gacy, James
Cook County Jail
Chicago, IL 60430
mass murderer

**Galbraith, John
Kenneth**
30 Francis Ave.
Cambridge, MA 02138
economist

Galella, Ron
17 Glover Ave.
Yonkers, NY 10704
photojournalist

Gallen, Hugh J.
Office of the Governor
Concord, NH 03301
governor of New Hampshire

Gallo, Ernest & Julio
P.O. Box 1173
Modesto, CA 95353
winemakers

Gallup, George
53 Bank St.
Princeton, NJ 08540
public opinion statistician

**Gamblers
Anonymous**
2705¼ W. 8th St.
Los Angeles, CA 90005
*James J. Zeysing,
executive secretary*

Gandhi, Indira
Office of the Prime Minister
New Delhi, India
prime minister of India

Garagiola, Joe
c/o NBC TV
30 Rockefeller Plaza
New York, NY 10020
sports commentator

Garbo, Greta
450 E. 52nd St.
New York, NY 10022
actress

Gardiner, John
c/o Random House
201 E. 50th St.
New York, NY 10022
author

Gardner, John
2030 M St. NW
Washington DC 20036
*writer, founder of Common
Cause, former secretary of
health, education & welfare*

Gardner, Randy
4640 Glen Cove #6
Marina del Rey, CA 90021
figure skater

Garfunkel, Art
Art Garfunkel Enterprises
460 Park Ave.
New York, NY 10022
singer, songwriter

Garn, Edwin Jacob
Senate Office Building
Washington DC 20510
senator from Utah

Garner, James
c/o Robinson & Associates
132 S. Rodeo Drive
Beverly Hills, CA 90210
actor

Garrahy, Joseph J.
Office of the Governor
Providence, RI 02903
governor of Rhode Island

Garrett, Leif
c/o ICM
8899 Beverly Blvd.
Los Angeles, CA 90048
singer

Garriott, Owen K.
Space & Life Sciences
Johnson Space Center
Houston, TX 77058
astronaut

Garrison, Jim
710 Carondelet St.
New Orleans, LA 70130
*Kennedy assassination
conspiracy advocate*

Garson, Greer
10375 Wilshire Blvd.
Los Angeles, CA 90024
actress

Garvey, Steve
c/o Los Angeles Dodgers
1000 Elysian Park Ave.
Los Angeles, CA 90012
baseball player

Gay, George
P.O. Box 8088
Naples, FL 33941
*fighter pilot who flew
in first attack at
battle of Midway*

Gaynor, Gloria
c/o Polydor Records
810 7th Ave.
New York, Ny 10019
singer

Gaynor, Mitzi
610 N. Arden Drive
Beverly Hills, CA 90210
dancer, actress

**Geisel, General
Ernesto**
Office of the President
Brasilia, Brazil
president of Brazil

**General Accounting
Office**
441 G St. NW
Washington DC 20548
*Elmer B. Staats,
controller general*

Gennaro, Peter
115 Central Park N.
New York, NY 10023
choreographer

Gentry, Bobbie
c/o Wm. Morris
151 El Camino Drive
Beverly Hills, CA 90212
singer

George, Lynda Day
c/o Kohner-Levy Agency
9169 Sunset Blvd.
Los Angeles, CA 90069
actress

George, Phyllis
c/o Ed Hookstratten
9454 Wilshire Blvd. #M-11
Beverly Hills, CA 90212
actress

Georgiade, Dr.N.G.
Duke University
Durham, NC 27706
*plastic surgeon specializing
in head, neck, jaw & breast
reconstruction*

Gershwin, Ira
1021 N. Roxbury Drive
Beverly Hills, CA 90210
lyricist

Gerulaitas, Vitas
c/o International
Management Group
1 Erieview Plaza
Cleveland, OH 44114
tennis player

Getty, Jean Paul
Sutton Place (near Guildford)
Surrey, England
son of J. Paul Getty

Ghotbzadeh, Sadegh
Office of the Foreign Minister
Tehran, Iran
foreign minister of Iran

Giant, Jolly Green
Hazeltine Gales
Chaska, MN 55318
tall vegetable farmer

Gibb, Andy
c/o RSO Records
1775 Broadway
New York, NY 10019
singer

Gibran, Kahlil
160 W. Canton St.
Boston, MA 02118
philosopher

Gibson, Bob
P.O. Box 6426
Omaha, NE 68106
former baseball player

Gibson, Henry
c/o Wm. Morris
151 El Camino Drive
Beverly Hills, CA 90212
comedian

Gibson, Kenneth
City Hall, Office of the Mayor
Newark, NJ 07102
mayor of Newark

Gielgud, Sir John
c/o Arnold Weissberger
120 E. 56th St.
New York, NY 10022
actor

Gifford, Frank
c/o ABC TV
1330 Avenue of the Americas
New York, NY 10019
sportscaster

Gilbert, Melissa
c/o NBC TV
3000 Alameda Ave.
Burbank, CA 91505
actress

Gillespie, Dizzy
c/o Associated Booking
Corporation
445 Park Ave.
New York, NY 10019
jazz trumpet player

Gimbel, Bruce A.
635 Madison Ave.
New York, NY 10022
department store executive

Gingold, Hermione
405 E. 54th St.
New York, NY 10022
actress

Gino's Fast Foods
215 Church Road
King of Prussia, PA 19406
Louis Fischer, president

Ginsberg, Allen
490 Park Ave.
Patterson, NJ 07504
poet

Giovando, Gualtiero
Via Fontana Ampia
12069 Santa Vittoria d'Alba
Prov. Cuneo, Italy
*developed techniques for
saving endangered species of
orchids*

**Girls Scouts of
America**
830 3rd Ave.
New York, NY 10022
*Frances Hesselbein,
executive director*

Gish, Lillian
430 E. 57th St.
New York, NY 10022
actress

Glaser, Dr. G.H.
Yale University
206 Elm St.
New Haven, CT 06520
*neurologist specializing in
epilepsy*

**Glaser, Paul-
Michael**
c/o Chasin-Park-Citron
9255 Sunset Blvd.
Los Angeles, CA 90069
actor

Gleason, Jackie
7215 W. 20th Ave.
Hialeah, FL 33014
entertainer

Glenister, Patricia
Leicester, England
*holds world record for go-go
dancing (110 hours)*

Glenn, John H. Jr.
Senate Office Building
Washington DC 20510
*senator from Ohio, former
astronaut*

Gobel, George
c/o Richard Fulton Inc.
850 7th Ave.
New York, NY 10019
entertainer

Godfrey, Arthur
c/o Wm. Morris
1350 Avenue of the Americas
New York, NY 10019
entertainer

Godwin, Ermon Jr.
Dunn, NC 28334
*organizer of National
Hollerin' Contest*

Godwin, Sir Harry
30 Barton Road
Cambridge
CB3 9LF, England
botanist

Godunov, Alexandr
c/o American Ballet Theatre
888 7th Ave.
New York, NY 10019
ballet dancer

Goldberg, Arthur
1101 17th St. NW
Washington DC 20036
*attorney, ambassador
at large*

Goldberg, Leonard
c/o 20th Century Fox
10201 W. Pico Blvd.
Los Angeles, CA 90064
producer

Goldsboro, Bobby
c/o Jan Kurtis
Box 226, Franklin Pike
Brentwood, TN 37027
singer, songwriter

Goldschmidt, Neil
400 7th St. NW
Washington DC 20590
secretary of transportation

Goldsmith, Jerry
c/o BMI Inc.
40 W. 57th St.
New York, NY 10019
composer

Goldstein, Al
116 W. 14th St.
New York, NY 10011
editor and publisher of Screw Magazine

Goldwater, Barry M.
Senate Office Building
Washington DC 20510
senator from Arizona

The Gong Show
6430 Sunset Blvd.
Hollywood, CA 90028
Diane Fell, talent coordinator

Gonzales, Pancho
c/o Caesar's Palace
Tennis Shop
3570 Las Vagas Blvd.
Las Vegas, NV 89109
tennis pro

Goodman, Benny
200 E. 66th St.
New York, NY 10021
conductor, clarinetist

B.F. Goodrich Co.
500 S. Main St.
Akron, OH 44318
O. Pendleton Thomas, president

Goodyear Tire & Rubber Company
1144 E. Market St.
Akron, OH 44316
Russell deYoung, president

Goolagong, Evonne
c/o International
Management Group
1 Erieview Plaza
Cleveland, OH 44114
tennis player

Gordon, Gale
c/o Rose, Newman &
Guterman
8530 Wilshire Blvd. #210
Beverly Hills, CA 90210
actor

Gordon, Ruth
P.O. Box 585
Edgartown, MA 02539
actress

Gordy, Berry
c/o Motown Records
6255 Sunset Blvd.
Hollywood, CA 90028
founder & chairman, Motown

Gorme, Eydie
P.O. Box 5140
Beverly Hills, CA 90210
singer

Gorney, Karen Lynn
c/o Creative Artists Agency
1888 Century Park E.
Suite 1400
Los Angeles, CA 90067
actress

Gortner, Marjoe
c/o ICM
8899 Beverly Blvd.
Los Angeles, CA 90048
actor, former evangelist

Gossett, Louis Jr.
c/o Wm. Morris
151 El Camino Drive
Beverly Hills, CA 90212
actor

Gould, Elliott
c/o Rogers & Cowan
9665 Wilshire Blvd.
Beverly Hills, CA 90212
actor

Goulding, Raymond
420 Lexington Ave.
New York, NY 10017
comedian (of Bob & Ray)

Goulet, Robert
c/o Creative Artists Agency
1888 Century Park E.
Suite 1400
Los Angeles, CA 90067
singer, actor

Grabb, Dr.W.
University of Michigan
Ann Arbor, MI 48109
plastic surgeon specializing in cleft lip and palate repair

Grable, Ned
P.O. Box 34
Twelve Mile, IN 46988
organizer of lawn mower races

Grace, Princess (of Monaco)
The Palace
Principality of Monaco
princess, former actress

Grade, Sir Lew
17 Great Cumberland Place
London, W1A 1AG
England
producer

Graham, Billy
1300 Harmon Place
Minneapolis, MN 55403
evangelist

Graham, Katherine
c/o *Washington Post*
1150 15th St. NW
Washington DC 20071
publisher

Graham, Martha
316 E. 63rd St.
New York, NY 10021
choreographer

Graham, Robert
Office of the Governor
Tallahassee, FL 32304
governor of Florida

Graham, Virginia
c/o Pinnacle Books
275 Madison Ave.
New York, NY 10016
former television commentator

Grant, Hank
c/o *Hollywood Reporter*
6715 Sunset Blvd.
Hollywood, CA 90028
entertainment columnist

Grant, Cary
P.O. Box 551
Beverly Hills, CA 90210
actor

Grant, Lee
c/o ICM
8899 Beverly Blvd.
Los Angeles, CA 90048
actress

Grassle, Karen
c/o ICPR
9255 Sunset Blvd.
Los Angeles, CA 90069
actress

Grasso, Ella
Office of the Governor
State Capitol
Hartford, CT 06115
governor of Connecticut

Grateful Dead
P.O. Box 1065
San Rafael, CA 94902
music group

Gravel, Mike
Senate Office Building
Washington DC 20510
senator from Alaska

Graves, Peter
c/o Fred Barman Associates
P.O. Box 2087
Beverly Hills, CA 90213
actor

Gray, Barry
888 7th Ave.
New York, NY 10019
late-night radio commentator

Gray Panthers
3700 Chestnut St.
Philadelphia, PA 19104
Margaret Kuhn, national convener

Gray, L. Patrick
Sindlay Way
Stonington, CT 06378
former FBI director

Greco, Jose
c/o Kolmar-Luth
Entertainment Inc.
1776 Broadway
New York, NY 10019
dancer

Green, Al
c/o The Music Factory Inc.
3208 Winchester Road
Memphis, TN 38118
singer

Green, John
903 N. Bedford Drive
Beverly Hills, CA 90210
composer

Greenamyer, Darryl
P.O. Box 5548
Mission Hills, CA 91345
*piloted aircraft to greatest
recorded height above earth*

Greenberg, Hank
1129 Miradero Road
Beverly Hills, CA 90210
*member of baseball
Hall of Fame*

Greenberg, Joanne
29221 Rainbow Hills Road
Golden, CO 80401
author

Greenburg, Dan
323 E. 50th St.
New York, NY 10022
author

Greene, Lorne
c/o Grossman-Stalmaster
Agency
8730 Sunset Blvd. #405
Hollywood, CA 90046
actor

Greene, Shecky
1245 Rancho Drive
Las Vegas, NV 89106
comedian

Greenspan, Alan
New York University
New York, NY 10011
economist

Greer, Germaine
c/o Farrar, Straus & Giroux
19 Union Square W.
New York, NY 10003
author, feminist

Gregory, Cynthia
c/o American Ballet Theatre
888 7th Ave.
New York, NY 10019
ballerina

Gregory, Dick
Long Pond Road
Manomet, MA 02345
comedian, civil rights activist

Gregory, James
c/o ICM
8899 Beverly Blvd.
Los Angeles, CA 90048
actor

Grey, Joel
c/o Wm. Morris
151 El Camino Drive
Beverly Hills, CA 90212
entertainer, actor

**Greyhound
Company**
Greyhound Tower
Phoenix, AZ 85077
Gerald Trautman, president

Griffin, Merv
1541 N. Vine St.
Hollywood, CA 90028
talk show host

**The Merv
Griffin Show**
1541 N. Vine St.
Hollywood, CA 90028
*Don Kane, talent
coordinator*

Griffith, Andy
c/o Richard O. Linke
Associates
4405 Riverside Drive #103
Burbank, CA 91505
actor

**Grigsby, Johnson
Van Dyke**
Marion County Home
Indianapolis, IN 46202
*world's longest prisoner
(incarcerated for 68 years)*

Grimes, Tammy
c/o ICM
8899 Beverly Blvd.
Los Angeles, CA 90048
actress

**Groebli, Werner
(Mr. Frick)**
2171 Campus Drive #340
Irvine, CA 92715
figure skater

Groh, David
c/o Phil Gersh
222 N. Canon Drive
Beverly Hills, CA 90210
actor

Grossinger, Paul
Grossinger Hotel
Grossinger, NY 12734
hotel executive

Grotowski, Jerzy
TEATR Laboratorium
50-101 Wroclaw
Rynek Ratusz 27,
Poland
director and acting teacher

Ground Saucer Watch
13238 N. 7th Drive
Phoenix, AZ 85029
William Spaulding, director

Grunwald, Henry Anatole
c/o *Life Magazine*
Time/Life Building
Rockefeller Center
New York, NY 10020
editor-in-chief, Time/Life magazine divisions

Guard, Dave
107 Degas Road
Portola Valley, CA 94025
musician (former member of The Kingston Trio)

Guardino, Harry
c/o ICM
8899 Beverly Blvd.
Los Angeles, CA 90048
actor

Gucci, Aldo
689 5th Ave.
New York, NY 10022
retail store executive

Guest, Paul
Environmental Consulting Office
31 Clerkenwell Close
London, EC 1R OAT
England
director of world assn. for celebration of year 2000

Guichard, Charles
21130 Wardell Road
Saratoga, CA 95070
seeker of buried treasure

Guidry, Ron
Yankee Stadium
Bronx, NY 10451
baseball player

Guillaume, Robert
c/o Wm. Morris
151 El Camino Drive
Beverly Hills, CA 90212
actor

Guiness, Sir Alec
Kettlebrook Meadows
Steep Marsh Petersfield
Hampshire, England
actor

Guinness Book of World Records
Sterling Publishing Company
2 Park Ave.
New York, NY 10016
Norm McWhirter, editor

Gulf Oil Company
P.O. Box 1166
Pittsburgh, PA 15230
Bob R. Dorsay, chief executive

Gulf Oil Corp.
Gulf Oil Building
Pittsburgh, PA 15219
Jerry McAfee, president

Gulf & Western Corporation
1 Gulf & Western Plaza
New York, NY 10023
Charles G. Bluhdorn, president

Gunn, Moses
c/o Arcara, Bauman & Hiller
Artists Managers
9220 Sunset Blvd.
Los Angeles, CA 90069
director, actor

Guthrie, Arlo
c/o Harold Levanthal
Mgmt. Company
250 W. 57th St. #1304
New York, NY 10019
singer, songwriter

Guthrie, Gary
WAKY Radio
Louisville, KY 40201
disc jockey who first mixed Neil Diamond and Barbra Streisand on "You Don't Bring Me Flowers"

Guthrie, Janet
343 E. 30th St. #12N
New York, NY 10016
race driver

Gwynne, Fred
Hook Road
Bedford, NY 10506
actor

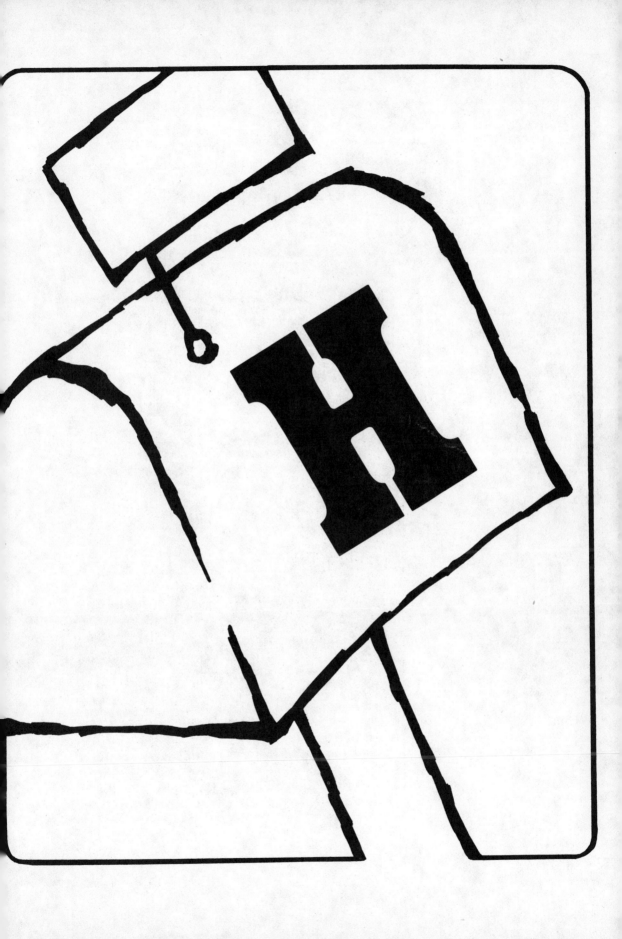

Haber, Joyce
c/o *Los Angeles Magazine*
1888 Century Park E.
Los Angeles, CA 90067
writer

Hack, Shelley
c/o Marty Litke
360 N. Bedford Drive
Suite 405
Beverly Hills, CA 90210
actress, model

Hackett, Buddy
c/o Creative Artists Agency
1888 Century Park E.
Suite 1400
Los Angeles, CA 90067
entertainer

Hackett, Joan
c/o Kimble-Parseghian
9255 Sunset Blvd.
Los Angeles, CA 90069
actress

Hackman, Gene
c/o ICM
8899 Beverly Blvd.
Los Angeles, CA 90048
actor

Haggard, Merle
Hag, Inc.
3844 River Blvd.
Bakersfield, CA 93305
singer, songwriter

Haggerty, Dan
c/o Wm. Morris
151 El Camino Drive
Beverly Hills, CA 90212
actor

Hagman, Larry
c/o CBS TV
7800 Beverly Blvd.
Los Angeles, CA 90036
actor

Haig, Alexander
United Technologies Bldg.
Hartford, CT 06101
U.S. Army general, former Nixon aide

Hailey, Arthur
c/o Seaway Authors Ltd.
1 pl. ville Marie Suite 1609
Montreal PQ, H3B 2B6
Canada
author

Halaby, Najeeb
640 5th Ave.
New York, NY 10019
financier

Haldeman, H.R.
443 N. McCadden Place
Los Angeles, CA 90004
former Nixon aide, convicted Watergate figure

Haley, Alex
P.O. Box 2907
San Francisco, CA 94126
author

Haley, Jack Jr.
1443 Devlin Drive
Los Angeles, CA 90069
producer

Hall & Oates
c/o Champion Entertainment
Organization
105 W. 55th St. Suite 7A
New York, NY 10019
music duet

Hall, Gus
c/o American Communist
Party
235 W. 23rd St.
New York, NY 10011
president, American Communist Party

Hall, Monty
6430 Sunset Blvd.
Los Angeles, CA 90028
television host, producer

Hall, Sir Peter Reginald Frederick
The Wall House
Mongewall Park
Wallingford
Berks, England
theatre, opera, and film director

Hallmark Cards Inc.
25th & McGee
Kansas City, MO 64108
Joyce Hall, publisher

Halstead, Dirk
Time-Life Building
Room 2850
New York, NY 10020
former White House photographer

Halston
(Roy Halston Frowick)
645 5th Ave.
New York, NY 10020
fashion designer

Hamel, Alan
c/o Brandon & Rodgers
9046 Sunset Blvd. Suite 201
Los Angeles, CA 90069
actor

Hamill, Dorothy
c/o Management III
9744 Wilshire Blvd.
Beverly Hills, CA 90212
figure skater

Hamill, Mark
c/o The Sackheim Agency
9301 Wilshire Blvd.
Suite 606
Beverly Hills, CA 90210
actor

Hamill, Pete
220 E. 42nd St.
New York, NY 10017
journalist

Hamilton, Charles
25 E. 77th St.
New York, NY 10021
*world's foremost autograph
collector and dealer*

Hamilton, George
c/o Contemporary-Korman
Artists
132 Lasky Drive
Beverly Hills, CA 90212
actor

Hamilton, Margaret
c/o Thomas Agency
22 E. 60th St.
New York, NY 10022
actress

Hamlisch, Marvin
c/o Rogers & Cowan
3 E. 54th St.
New York, NY 10022
composer

**Hammer, Dr.
Armand**
P.O. Box 107
Colts Neck, NJ 07722
oil executive

Hammond, Jay S.
Office of the Governor
Juneau, Alaska 99811
governor of Alaska

Hampshire, Susan
c/o Chatto & Linnitt Ltd.
113 Wardour St.
London W1 England
actress

Hampton, Lionel
3808 W. Adams Blvd.
Los Angeles, CA 90018
conductor

Hancock, Herbie
c/o Adam's Dad
Management
827 Folsom St.
San Francisco, CA 94107
jazz musician, composer

**John Hancock
Insurance Co.**
John Hancock Plaza
Boston, MA 02117
Gerhard Bleichen, president

Hand, Karl J.
P.O. Box 6987
Buffalo, NY 14240
*editor of Nightrider, official
publicaton of Ku Klux Klan*

Hanes Corporation
P.O. Box 5416
Winston-Salem, NC 27103
Gordon Hanes, president

Hanna, Walt
618 N. Maple Drive
Beverly Hills, CA 90210
Jimmy Carter look-alike

Hanna, William
c/o Hanna-Barbera
Productions Inc.
3400 W. Cahuenga Blvd.
Hollywood, CA 90068
producer

Hanrahan, Jack
c/o Random House
201 E. 50th St.
New York, NY 10022
writer

**Hansen, Elisa and
Lisa**
University of Utah
1400 E. 2 South
Salt Lake City, UT 84112
separated Siamese twins

Hansen, Gary
Gary Hansen Cakes
1060 S. Fairfax Ave.
Los Angeles, CA 90019
custom cake decorator

Hansen, Irwin
68 E. 79th St.
New York, NY 10021
cartoonist

Hanson, Kitty
220 E. 42nd St.
New York, NY 10017
journalist

Harburg, Edgar "Yip"
551 5th Ave.
New York, NY 10017
lyricist

Harcourt, Brace, Jovanovich Inc.
757 3rd Ave.
New York, NY 10017
William Jovanovich, publisher

Hardy, Joseph
P.O. Box 238
Radio City Station
New York, NY 10019
actor

Hargrove, Linda (Ann)
809 18th Ave. S.
Nashville, TN 37203
songwriter

Harley-Davidson Company
3700 W. Juneau Ave.
Milwaukee, WI 53201
John A. Davidson, president

Harper & Row Publishing Co.
10 E. 53rd St.
New York, NY 10022
John Cowles, president

Harper, Valerie
c/o Pickwick
9744 Wilshire Blvd.
Beverly Hills, CA 90212
actress

Harriman, Averell
3038 N. St.
Washington DC 20007
former ambassador and New York governor

Harrington, Pat
c/o Druxman
6464 Sunset Blvd. #760
Los Angeles, CA 90028
actor

Harris, Barbara
c/o Robinson & Associates
132 S. Rodeo Drive
Beverly Hills, CA 90212
actress

Harris, Brick
Rt. 5, P.O. Box 196-1A
Priest Lake, ID 83856
organizer of broom hockey games

Harris, Eddie
c/o Pilgrim Management Productions
10 W. 66th St.
New York, NY 10023
saxophonist

Harris, Emily
California Institute for Women
Frontera, CA 91720
convicted kidnapper and bank robber

Harris, Emmylou
c/o Getz-Tickner Organization
8380 Melrose Ave. #305
Los Angeles, CA 90069
singer

Harris, Hemphill
Hemphill Harris Travel Corporation
10100 Santa Monica Blvd.
Suite 2060
Los Angeles, CA 90067
unusual vacation organizer

Harris, Julie
c/o Wm. Morris
1350 Avenue of the Americas
New York, NY 10019
actress

Harris, Louis
630 5th Ave.
New York, NY 10020
public opinion analyst

Harris, Patricia
451 7th St. SW
Washington DC 20410
*secretary of health, education
and welfare*

Harris, Richard
c/o Creative Artists Agency
1888 Century Park E.
Suite 1400
Los Angeles, CA 90067
actor

Harris, Susan
c/o ABC TV
4151 Prospect Ave.
Hollywood, CA 90027
writer, producer

Harris, William
California Institute for Men
Chino, CA 91720
*convicted kidnapper and
bank robber*

Harrison, George
c/o Dark Horse Records
3300 Warner Blvd.
Burbank, CA 91510
musician, composer

Harrison, Gregory
c/o 20th Century Fox
10201 W. Pico Blvd.
Los Angeles, CA 90064
actor

Harrison, Rex
c/o Wm. Morris
151 El Camino Drive
Beverly Hills, CA 90212
actor

Harry, Deborah
c/o Chrysalis
115 E. 57th St.
New York, NY 10022
*lead singer of rock group
Blondie*

Hart, Gary W.
Senate Office Building
Washington DC 20510
senator from Colorado

Hart, John
c/o Publishers-Hall
Syndicate
401 N. Wabash Ave.
Chicago, IL 60611
cartoonist

**Hartford,
Huntington**
600 3rd Ave.
New York, NY10016
financier

Hartford, John
c/o Stone County Inc
2104 Glenarm Place
Denver, CO 80205
songwriter

Hartke, Vance
6500 Kerns Court
Falls Church, VA 22044
former senator

Hartley, Mariette
10337 Wilshire Blvd.
Los Angeles, CA 90024
actress

Hartman, David
c/o Trascott, Alyson & Craig
222 Cedar Lane
Teaneck, NJ 07666
television host

Harvey, Paul
360 N. Michigan Ave.
Chicago, IL 60601
news analyst

**Haskell, Arnold
Lionel**
6A Cavendish Crescent
Bath, Avon
BA, ZUG England
ballet school governor

Hatch, Orrin
Senate Office Building
Washington DC 20510
senator from Utah

Hatch, Richard
c/o Wm. Morris
151 El Camino Drive
Beverly Hills, CA 90212
actor

Hatfield, Mark O.
Senate Office Building
Washington DC 20510
senator from Oregon

**Hausen, Hans
Magnus**
Armas Lindgrensvag 7
00570 Helsinki 57
Finland
geologist

Hauson, Howard A.
U.S. Tax Court
Washington DC 20217
chief judge of U.S. Tax Court

Hawn, Goldie
c/o Wm. Morris
151 El Camino Drive
Beverly Hills ,CA 90212
actress

Hayakawa, S.I.
Senate Office Building
Washington DC 20510
senator from California

Hayden, Tom
c/o Campaign for Economic
Democracy
304 S. Broadway #501
Los Angeles, CA 90013
political activist

Hayes, Bill
4528 Beck Ave.
No. Hollywood, CA 91602
actor

Hayes, Helen
Kahaik Farms
Nyack, NY 10960
actress

Hayes, Isaac
c/o Forest Hamilton
Personal Management
9229 Sunset Blvd. #700
Los Angeles, CA 90069
composer

Hayes, Susan Seaforth
c/o Anita de Thomas
& Associates
1880 Century Park E.
Los Angeles, CA 90067
actress

Hayes, Woody
Ohio State University
Converse Hall
2121 Tuttle Park Place
Columbus, OH 43210
former football coach

Haynsworth, Clement
Boxwood Lane
Greenville, SC 29601
judge

Hays, Wayne
P.O. Box 95
St. Clairsville, OH 43950
former congressman

Hayworth, Rita
c/o Contemporary-Korman
Artists
132 Lasky Drive
Beverly Hills, CA 90212
actress

Hazan, Marcella
155 E. 76th St.
New York, NY 10021
*Italian chef and
cooking teacher*

Head, Edith
c/o Universal Studios
Universal City, CA 91608
costume designer

Hearst, Catherine Campbell
Hillsborough, CA 94010
civic worker

Hearst Shaw, Patricia
110 5th St.
San Francisco, CA 94103
*victim of controversial
kidnap case*

Hearst, William Randolph
110 5th St.
San Francisco, CA 91403
publisher

Hebrew National Kosher Foods
5880 Maurice Ave.
Maspeth, NY 11378
Isidore Pines, president

Heflin, Howell T.
Senate Office Building
Washington DC 20510
senator from Alabama

Hefner, Hugh M.
c/o Playboy Enterprises
919 N. Michigan Ave.
Chicago, IL 60611
publisher

Hegyes, Robert
c/o ABC TV
4151 Prospect Ave.
Los Angeles, CA 90027
actor

Heifetz, Jascha
c/o Beverly Crest Hotel
Beverly Hills, CA 90210
violinist

Heineken Brewery
Heineken NV
Postbox 28
Amsterdam, Netherands
Alfred Heineken, president

Heinz Food Co.
1062 Progress St.
Pittsburgh, PA 15212
*Henry J. Heinz II and
Henry J. Heinz III, directors*

Heinz, H. John III
Senate Office Building
Washington DC 20510
senator from Pennsylvania

Hekmat, Ali Asghar
Pol-o Roumi
Chemiran
Teheran, Iran
Iranian politician

Heller, Joseph
c/o Simon & Schuster
630 5th Ave.
New York, NY 10020
author

Heller, Dr. P.
University of Illinois
Chicago, IL 60612
*specialist in chemotherapy
and hematology*

Hellman, Lillian
630 Park Ave.
New York, NY 10021
playwright

Helmond, Katherine
c/o ABC TV
4151 Prospect Ave.
Los Angeles, CA 90027
actress

Helms, Jesse
Senate Office Building
Washington DC 20510
senator from North Carolina

Helms, Richard
c/o Safee Company
1627 K St. NW Suite 402
Washington DC 20006
former CIA director

**Helpmann, Sir
Robert Murray**
c/o The Royal Ballet
Convent Garden
London, WC 2, England
choreographer, actor

**Hemingway,
Margeaux**
c/o Faberge, Inc.
1345 Avenue of the Americas
New York, NY 10019
actress, model

Hemingway, Mariel
c/o ICM
40 W. 57th St.
New York, NY 10019
actress

Hemsley, Sherman
c/o CBS TV
7800 Beverly Blvd.
Los Angeles, CA 90036
actor

**Henderson,
Florence**
c/o The Artists Agency
190 Canon Drive
Beverly Hills, CA 90210
actress, singer

**Henderson,
Oran (Col.)**
Penn State Council
of Civil Defense
Harrisburg, PA 17120
involved in My Lai massacre

Henner, Marilu
c/o ABC TV
4151 Prospect Ave.
Los Angeles, CA 90027
actress

Henning, Doug
c/o Jerry Goldstein
9200 Sunset Blvd.
Los Angeles, CA 90069
illusionist

Hendrie, Joseph
Nuclear Regulatory
Commission
Washington DC 20555
chairman

Henry, Justin
c/o Sam Cohn
ICM
40 W. 57th St.
New York, NY 10019
actor

Hensel, Witold
Marszalkowska 84/92
Ap 109, 00-514
Warsaw, Poland
archaeologist

Henson, Jim
c/o ITC Entertainment
115 E. 57th St.
New York, NY 10022
creator of the Muppets

Henze, Hans Werner
La Leprara
00047 Marino
Rome, Italy
composer, conductor

Hepburn, Audrey
c/o Kurt Frings
9440 Santa Monica Blvd.
Beverly Hills, CA 90210
actress

Hepburn, Katherine
P.O. Box 17154
West Hartford, CT 06117
actress

Herman, Jerry
55 Central Park W.
New York, NY 10023
composer, lyricist

Herman, Woody
c/o Hermie Dressel
Entertainment
161 W. 5th St.
New York, NY 10019
orchestra leader

Hernon, Patrick
12 Editha Mansions
Edith Grove
London, SW 10, England
artist

Herschler, Ed
Office of the Governor
Cheyenne, WY 82002
governor of Wyoming

Hershey, Barbara
c/o Chasin-Park-Citron
9255 Sunset Blvd.
Los Angeles, CA 90069
actress

Hershey, Lenore
c/o *Ladies Home Journal*
641 Lexington Ave.
New York, NY 10022
editor-in-chief

Hertz *Rent-A-Car*
660 Madison Ave.
New York, NY 10021
Frank Olson, president

Hertzberg, Rabbi Arthur
147 Tenafly Road
Englewood, NJ 07631
president, American Jewish Conference

Herzog, Arthur
230 E. 50th St.
New York, NY 10022
author

Herzog, General Chaim
Permanent Mission of Israel
to United Nations
800 2nd Ave.
New York, NY 10017
lawyer, military expert

Hess, Rudolf
Spandau Prison
Berlin, Germany
assistant to Hitler

Hess, Dr. Werner
German National
Tourist Office
630 5th Ave.
New York, NY 10026
stress specialist

Hesselbach, Walter
Bank fur
Gemeinwirtschaft A.G.
6 Frankfurt am Main
Mainzer Landstrasse 16-24
Federal Republic of Germany
banker and company director

Hesseman, Howard
c/o Wally Hiller
9220 Sunset Blvd. Suite 202
Los Angeles, CA 90069
actor

Heston, Charlton
c/o Chasin-Park-Citron
9255 Sunset Blvd.
Los Angeles, CA 90069
actor

Heyerdahl, Thor
Colla Micheri
Laigueglia, Italy
anthropologist, author

Hibernia Bank
1 Jones St.
San Francisco, CA 94102
bank robbed by Patricia Hearst
Michael Tobin, president

Hickel, Walter
Traveler's Inn
Hotel Captain Cook
Shopping Center
510 L St. Suite 607
Anchorage, AK 99501
former secretary of the interior

Hill, Arthur
1515 Club View Drive
Los Angeles, CA 90024
actor

Hicks, Louise Day
493 Broadway
South Boston, MA 02127
former congresswoman

Hill, Sandy
c/o ABC TV
1330 Avenue of the Americas
New York, NY 10019
talk show hostess

Hillman, John
1007 Golfview Drive Apt. A
Carmel, IN 46032
dog show judge

Hills Brothers Coffee, Inc.
265 Union St.
San Francisco, CA 94133
Rueben Hills, president

Hilton Hotel Corp.
9880 Wilshire Blvd.
Beverly Hills, CA 90210
Barron Hilton, president

Hirohito, Emperor
Emperor's Palace
Tokyo, Japan
emperor of Japan

Hirsch, Judd
c/o Guild Management Corp.
10203 Santa Monica Blvd.
Los Angeles, CA 90067
actor

Hirschfield, Al
229 W. 43rd St.
New York, NY 10036
cartoonist

Hirt, Al
Al Hirt Enterprises
809 St. Louis St.
New Orleans, LA 70112
musician

Hiss, Alger
c/o Helen Buttenwieser
575 Madison Ave.
New York, NY 10022
involved in famous espionage case

Hitchcock, Sir Alfred
c/o Universal Studios
Universal City, CA 91608
director

Hodes, Arthur
232 Berry St.
Park Forest, IL 60466
jazz pianist

Hoff, Syd
P.O. Box 2463
Miami Beach, FL 33140
author

Hoffa, James P. Jr.
Guardian Building
500 Griswold
Detroit, MI 48226
son of late Jimmy Hoffa

Hoffman, Abbie
c/o Gerald Lefcourt
299 Broadway
New York, NY 10017
socio-political activist

Hoffman, Dustin
c/o Sweet Wall Productions
315 E. 65th St.
New York, NY 10022
actor

Hoffman, Julius J.
Illinois District Court
219 Dearborn St.
Chicago, IL 60604
judge who presided over Chicago Seven trial

Holbrook, Hal
c/o The Artists Agency
190 N. Canon Drive
Beverly Hills, CA 90210
actor

Holden, William
c/o Grodean-Friedman Agency Inc.
9229 Sunset Blvd.
Los Angeles, CA 90069
actor

Holder, Geoffrey
215 W. 92nd St.
New York, NY 10025
choreographer

Holiday Inn Motels
3742 Lamar Ave.
Memphis, TN 38118
Kemmons Wilson, president

Holland, Tim
53 E. 66th St.
New York, NY 10021
*professional backgammon
player and teacher*

Hollander, Xaviera
c/o *Penthouse* Magazine
909 3rd Ave.
New York, NY 10022
columnist, author

**Hollerer, Walter
Friedrich**
heerstr. 99
Berlin 19
Federal Republic of Germany
German writer and critic

Holliday, Polly
c/o CBS TV
7800 Beverly Blvd.
Los Angeles, CA 90036
actress

Holliman, Earl
c/o Creative Artists Agency
1888 Century Park E.
#1400
Los Angeles, CA 90067
actor

Hollings, Ernest F.
Senate Office Building
Washington DC 20510
senator from South Carolina

Holloway, John
Queen's College
Cambridge, England
professor of modern English

Holloway, Sterling
137 N. Sycamore Ave.
Los Angeles, CA 90036
actor

Holm, Celeste
88 Central Park W.
New York, NY 10023
actor

Holtzman, Elizabeth
House Office Building
Washington DC 20215
U.S. representative

**Honeywell
Company**
Honeywell Plaza
Minneapolis, MN 55408
Stephen Keating, president

Hooks, Benjamin L.
National Association for the
Advancement of
Colored People
1790 Broadway
New York, NY 10019
executive director

Hoover Company
101 E. Maple St. N.
Canton, OH 44720
Joseph Hoover, president

Hope, Bob
3808 Riverside Drive
Suite 10
Burbank, CA 91505
entertainer

Hopkins, Anthony
c/o Chasin-Park-Citron
9255 Sunset Blvd.
Los Angeles, CA 90069
actor

Hopper, Dennis
P.O. Box 1889
Taos, NM 87571
actor

**Horn &
Hardart Company**
1163 Avenue of the Americas
New York, NY 10036
*Frederick Guterman,
president*

**Hornby, Lesley
(Twiggy)**
c/o Mercury Records
IBM Plaza
Chicago, IL 60611
actress, singer

Horne, Lena
1200 S. Arlington Ave.
Los Angeles, CA 90024
singer

Horowitz, David
4 Lamed Heh St.
Jerusalem, Israel
economist

Horowitz, David
c/o NBC TV
3000 W. Alameda
Burbank, CA 91523
consumer ombudsman

Horowitz, Vladimir
c/o Shaw Concerts
1995 Broadway
New York, NY 10023
concert pianist

Houseman, John
565 S. Mountain Road
New York, NY 10956
actor

Howald, Professor Oscar
Stablistrasse 19
5200 Brugg
Switzerland
agricultural economist and professor

Howar, Barbara
c/o CBS News
524 57th St.
New York, NY 10019
columnist

Howard, Ron
c/o Larry Frank
1801 Avenue of the Stars
Los Angeles, CA 90067
actor

Howland, Beth
c/o CBS TV
7800 Beverly Blvd.
Los Angeles, CA 90036
actress

Hsiao-p'ing, Teng
Peking, China
vice-premier of China

Hua Kuo-Feng
Central Committee of
the Chinese Communist
Party of China
Peking, China
chairman, Chinese Communist Party

Huant, Ernest Albin Camille
9 avenue Niel
75017 Paris, France
philosopher

Hubbard, L. Ron
210 S. Fort Harrison Ave.
Clearwater, FL 33516
founder of Scientology

Hubley, John
Hubley Studio Inc.
815 Park Ave.
New York, NY 10021
animator

Hubley, Season
c/o Hanson & Schwam
9229 Sunset Blvd. Suite 603
Los Angeles, CA 90069
actress

Huddleston, Walter D.
Senate Office Building
Washington DC 20510
senator from Kentucky

Hudson, Rock
c/o Wm. Morris
151 El Camino Drive
Beverly Hills, CA 90212
actor

Hufstuder, Shirley
200 Independence Ave. SW
Washington DC 20201
secretary of education

Hughen, Walter
406 N. 3rd St.
Chipley, FL 32428
organizer of watermelon seed spitting contest

Hughes, Harry R.
Office of the Governor
Annapolis, MD 21404
governor of Maryland

Hughes Tool Co.
5425 Polk Ave.
Houston, TX 77023
Raymond Holliday, president

Humane Society of the United States
2100 L Street NW
Washington DC 20037
John A. Hoyt, president

Humperdinck, Englebert
c/o Harold Davidson
24-25 New Bond St.
London, England
singer

Humphrey, Gordon J.
Senate Office Building
Washington DC 20510
senator from New Hampshire

Humphrey, John Peters
1455 Sherbrook St.
Montreal, P.Q., Canada
Canadian international official

Humphrey, Muriel
550 N St. NW
Washington DC 20024
widow of Hubert Humphrey

Hunt, E. Howard
1245 NE 85th St.
Miami, FL 33138
convicted Watergate figure

Hunt, James B.
Office of the Governor
Raleigh, NC 27611
governor of North Carolina

Hunt, Lamar
c/o Kansas City Chiefs
One Arrowhead Drive
Kansas City, MO 64129
founder, American Football League

Hunter, Kim
42 Commerce St.
New York, NY 10014
actress

Hupp, Robert
Father Flanagan's
Boys' Home
Boys Town, NE 68010
director, Boys Town

Hussein, King
Amman, Jordan
king of Jordan

Huston, John
St. Clerans
Craughwall County
Galway, Ireland
director, actor

Hutton, Lauren
c/o Pickwick
545 Madison Ave.
New York, NY 10022
model, actress

Huxley, Hugh Esmor
Medical Research Council
Laboratory of
Molecular Biology
Hills Road
Cambridge, England
biologist

Hyde-White, Wilfrid
c/o Paramount TV
5451 Marathon St.
Hollywood, CA 90038
actor

Iakovos, (Archbishop)
810 E. 79th St.
New York, NY 10021
archbishop of Greek orthodox church

Ian, Janis
c/o Harcourt Powell Mgmt.
850 7th Ave. #701
New York, NY 10019
singer, songwriter

IBM Corporation
Armonk, NY 10504
Frank T. Cary, president

Ideal Toy Company
18410 Jamaica Ave.
Hollis, NY 11423
Lionel Weintraub, president

Information Please Almanac
57 W. 57th St.
New York, NY 10019
Theodore Dolmatch, editor and publisher

Ingels, Marty
7560 Hollywood Blvd.
Hollywood, CA 90046
actor, agent

Innis, Roy
200 W. 135th St.
New York, NY 10030
civil rights activist

Inouye, Daniel K.
Senate Office Building
Washington DC 20510
senator from Hawaii

International Association for Suicide Prevention
Suicide Prevention & Crisis Center
1811 Trousdale Road
Burlingame, CA 94010
Charlotte P. Ross, secretary-general

International Beer Tasting Society
801 Via Lido Sound
Newport Beach, CA 92663
Martin J. Lockney, director

International Council Against Bullfighting
13 Graystone Road
Tankerton, Kent CT5 2JY
England
Alfred Weirs, honorable secretary

International Creative Management
8899 Beverly Blvd.
Los Angeles, CA 90048
Marvin Josephson, president

International Federation of American Homing Pigeon Fanciers
107 Jefferson St.
Belmont Hills, PA 19004
Joe Rotondo, secretary-treasurer

International Frisbee Association
P.O. Box 970
San Gabriel, CA 91776
Dan Roddick, director

International Kiteflyers Association
321 E. 48th St.
New York, NY 10017
Will Yolen, president

International Olympic Committee
Chateau De Vidy
CH-1007 Lausanne
Switzerland
Monique Berlioux, director

Interstate Commerce Commission
12th St. & Constitution Ave. NW
Washington DC 20433
A. Daniel O'Neal, chairman

Ionesco, Eugene
14 rue de Rivoli
Paris 4e, France
playwright

Iordan, Iorgu
Str. Sofia 21
Bucharest, Romania
Romance philologist

Ireland, Jill
c/o ICPR
9255 Sunset Blvd.
Los Angeles, CA 90069
actress

Irving, Clifford
San Miguel Allende
Apartade 225
Mexico
fraudulent Howard Hughes
biographer

Irving, John
c/o Matson Company
22 E. 40th St.
New York, NY 10016
author

Irwin, James
c/o High Flight Foundation
5010 Edison Ave.
Colorado Springs, CO 80915
former astronaut

Italiaander, Rolf
Bruno Maximilian
St. Benedictstrasse 29
Hamburg, 13
Federal Republic of Germany
writer, ethnologist and
explorer

Ives, Burl
c/o Beakel-Jennings
427 Canon Drive #205
Beverly Hills, CA 90210
singer, actor

Jack, Wolfman
c/o Fred Amsel
215 S. La Cienega Blvd.
#200
Beverly Hills, CA 90211
disc jockey, television host

Jackson, "Bags"
c/o Ray Brown Music
1777 Vine St. #315
Hollywood, CA 90028
jazz musician

Jackson, Glenda
c/o Robinson & Associates
132 S. Rodeo Drive
Beverly Hills, CA 90210
actress

**Jackson, Henry
'Scoop"**
Senate Office Building
Washington DC 20510
senator from Washington

Jackson, Rev. Jesse
c/o Operation PUSH
930 E. 50th St.
Chicago, IL 60615
clergyman, social activist

Jackson, Kate
c/o Sandy Littman
1707 Clearview Ave.
Beverly Hills, CA 90210
actress

Jackson, Maynard
City Hall
Atlanta, GA 30303
mayor of Atlanta

Jackson, Michael
c/o Motown Records
6255 Sunset Blvd.
Hollywood, CA 90028
singer

Jackson, Reggie
c/o New York Yankees
Yankee Stadium
Bronx, NY 01451
baseball player

Jacksons, The
c/o Joe Jackson
6255 Sunset Blvd. #1023
Los Angeles, CA 90028
music group

Jacobi, Lou
c/o Wm. Morris
1350 Avenue of the Americas
New York, NY 10019
actor

Jacobs, Jim
c/o ICM
40 W. 57th St.
New York, NY 10019
playwright

Jacobs, Lawrence-Hilton
c/o ABC TV
4151 Prospect Ave.
Los Angeles, CA 90027
actor

Jadot Rev. Jean
3339 Massachusetts Ave. NW
Washington DC 20008
U.S. delegate to Roman Catholic Church

Jaffe, Leo
711 5th Ave.
New York, NY 10022
president, Columbia Pictures

Jaffe, Sam
c/o Tony Ford Agency
291 S. La Cienega Blvd.
Beverly Hills, CA 90211
actor

Jagger, Dean
c/o Progressive Artists Agency
400 S. Beverly Drive
Beverly Hills, CA 90212
actor

Jagger, Mick
c/o Sir Productions
130 W. 57th St.
New York, NY 10019
singer

Jaidah, Ali M.
OPEC
Karl Lueger – Ring 10
1010 Vienna 1, Austria
secretary-general, Organization of the Petroleum Exporting Countries

James, Fob
Office of the Governor
Montgomery, AL 36104
governor of Alabama

Janeway, Eliot
Janeway Research Company
15 E. 80th St.
New York, NY 10021
economist

Janklow, William
Office of the Governor
Pierre, SD 57501
governor of South Dakota

Jarvis, Howard
6221 Wilshire Blvd.
Los Angeles, CA 90048
tax revolt leader

Javits, Jacob
Senate Office Building
Washington DC 20510
senator from New York

Jaworski, Leon
Ella Lee Lane
Houston, TX 77027
prosecuting attorney in Watergate case

Jefferson Starship
c/o Bill Thompson
P.O. Box 99387
San Francisco, CA 94109
music group

Jenkins, George
740 Kingman Ave.
Santa Monica, CA 90402
stage designer, art director

Jenner, Bruce
c/o Sports Media Sales
1901 Avenue of the Stars
Los Angeles, CA 90067
athlete, sports commentator

Jennings, Peter
c/o ABC News
7 W. 66th St.
New York, NY 10023
journalist

Jennings, Waylon
c/o Media Consulting Corp.
50 W. 57th St. #1200
New York, NY 10019
singer

Jepsen, Roger W.
Senate Office Building
Washington DC 20510
senator from Iowa

Jessel, George
c/o Hillcrest Country Club
Los Angeles, CA 90067
actor, comedian

Jewish Defense League
1133 Broadway Room 310
New York, NY 10010
David Fisch, director

Jewison, Norman
c/o Julius Lefkowitz & Co.
9171 Wilshire Blvd. #420
Beverly Hills, CA 90210
producer, director

Joel, Billy
c/o Home Run
Management Co.
14 E. 60th St. #1210
New York, NY 10022
singer

John, Elton
c/o John Reid Enterprises
40 S. Audley St.
Mayfair, London
W1Y 5DH England
singer

John Paul II, Pope
Palazzo Apostolico Vaticano
Vatican City, Italy
pope

Johns, Dr. T.R.
University of Virginia
Charlottesville, VA 22904
neurologist specializing in myasthenia gravis

Johnson, Alexis
U.S. State Department
Washington DC 20520
chief negotiator for SALT talks

Johnson, Arte
2725 Bottlebrush Drive
Los Angeles, CA 90026
comedian, actor

Johnson, Ben
c/o Herb Tobias &
Associates
1901 Avenue of the Stars
#840
Los Angeles, CA 90067
actor

Johnson, Frank M.
U.S. District Court
Federal Building
Montgomery, AL 36105
judge, nominated for FBI director

Howard Johnson Motels & Restaurants
1 Howard Johnson Plaza
Boston, MA 02125
Howard B. Johnson, president

Johnson & Johnson
501 George St.
New Brunswick, NJ 08903
James Burke, president

Johnson, Lady Bird
c/o LBJ Library
2313 Red River
Austin, TX 78705
widow of Lyndon B. Johnson

Johnson, Philip
375 Park Ave.
New York, NY 10022
architect

Johnson, Dr. R.
Johns Hopkins Medical
School
601 N. Broadway
Baltimore, MD 21205
*neurologist specializing in
multiple sclerosis*

Johnson, Rafer
c/o The Mishkin Agency
9255 Sunset Blvd.
Los Angeles, CA 90069
actor, athlete

Johnson, Sonia
P.O. Box 233
Sterling Park, VA 22170
*ERA supporter excommuni-
cated from Mormon Church*

Johnson, Van
c/o Alan Foshko Associates
305 W. 52nd St.
New York, NY 10019
actor

Johnson, Virginia
4910 Forest Park Blvd.
St. Louis, MO 63108
sex therapist

Johnston, J. Bennett
Senate Office Building
Washington DC 20510
senator from Louisiana

Jones, Carolyn
c/o Lew Sherell Agency, Ltd.
7060 Hollywood Blvd.
Hollywood, CA 90028
actress

Jones, Dean
c/o Creative Artists Agency
1888 Century Park E.
Suite 1400
Los Angeles, CA 90067
actor

Jones, James Earl
19 Allen St.
New York, NY 10002
actor

Jones, Jennifer
c/o Wm. Morris
151 El Camino Drive
Beverly Hills ,CA 90212
actress

Jones, Parnelli
20550 Earl St.
Torrance, CA 90503
race driver

Jones, Quincy
c/o A & M Records
1416 N. La Brea Ave.
Hollywood, CA 90028
composer, conductor

Jones, Ricky Lee
c/o Warner Brothers Records
3300 Warner Blvd.
Burbank, CA 91510
singer

Jones, Shirley
c/o Aarons Entertainment
9665 Wilshire Blvd. #320
Beverly Hills, CA 90212
actress

Jones, Tom
c/o MAM
24-25 New Bond St.
London, England
singer

Jong, Erica
c/o Sterling Lord Agency
660 Madison Ave.
New York, NY 10021
author

Jordache
498 7th Ave.
New York, NY 10018
Avi Nakash, manufacturer

Jordan, Barbara
House Office Building
Washington DC 20515
U.S. representative

Jordan, Charles
General Motors Design Staff
Warren, MI 18090
automotive designer

Jordan, Hamilton
c/o The White House
1600 Pennsylvania Ave. NW
Washington DC 20500
presidential assistant

Jordan, Vernon
500 E. 52nd St.
New York, NY 10021
*president, National Urban
League*

Jourdan, Louis
c/o ICM
8899 Beverly Blvd.
Los Angeles, CA 90048
actor

Judge, Stanley
Hull
Humberside, England
*holds world record for eating
hard-boiled eggs (12 in 103
seconds)*

Judge, Thomas L.
Office of the Governor
Helena, MT 59601
governor of Montana

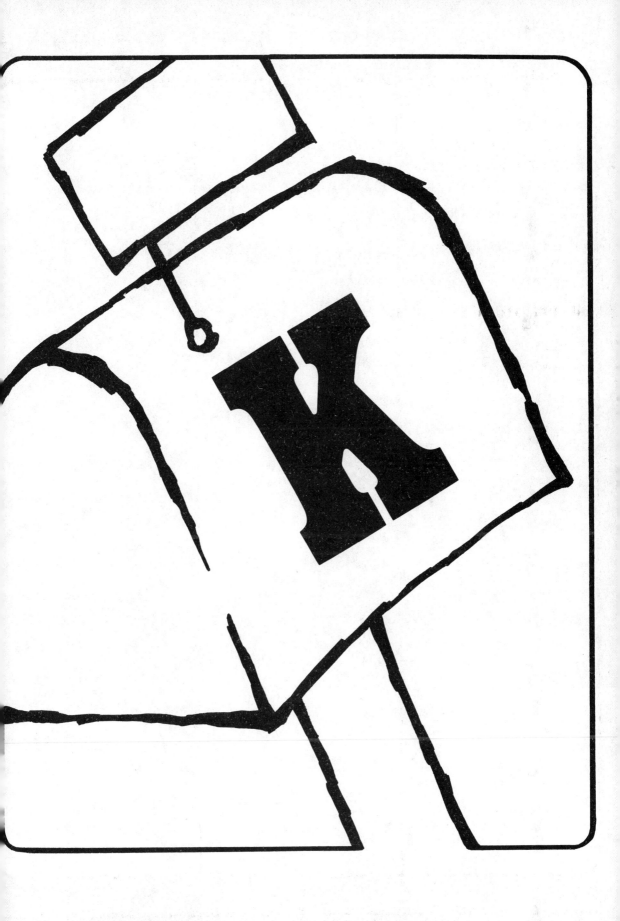

K Mart Company
3100 W. Big Beaver
Troy, MI 48084
Robert E. Dewar, president

Kahane, Rabbi Meir
Box 15117
Jerusalem, Israel
former member, Jewish Defense League

Kahn, Alfred E.
The White House
1600 Pennsylvania Ave. NW
Washington DC 20500
inflation fighter

Kahn, Herman
National Archives Advisory Council
Washington DC 20408
archivist

Kahn, Madeline
c/o Bert Padell
405 Park Ave.
New York, NY 10022
actress

Kai-shek, Madame Chiang
Lattingtown, NY 11560
widow of Chiang Kai-shek

Kalmbach, Herbert
1056 Santiago Drive
Newport Beach, CA 92660
former Nixon assistant

Kane, Carol
c/o Wm. Morris
1350 Avenue of the Americas
New York, NY 10019
actress

Kaplan, Gabriel
c/o L. Frank & Co.
1801 Avenue of the Stars
Los Angeles, CA 90067
actor, comedian

Karpov, Anatoly
c/o State Committee for Sports & Physical Culture of the USSR
Council of Ministers
Moscow, USSR
chess grand master

Karsh, Yousuf
18 E. 62nd St.
New York, NY 10021
photographer

Kassebaum, Nancy Landon
Senate Office Building
Washington DC 20510
senator from Kansas

Kassorla, Dr. Irene
1005 N. Beverly Drive
Beverly Hills, CA 90210
psychologist treating many Hollywood celebrities

Katzenbach, Nicholas
c/o IBM
Old Orchard Road
Armonk, NY 10504
attorney

Kaufman, Andy
c/o ABC TV
4151 Prospect Ave.
Los Angeles, CA 90027
actor

Kaufman, Sue
544 W. 86th St.
New York, NY 10028
author

Kavner, Julie
c/o MTM Productions
4024 Radford
Studio City, CA 91604
actress

Kaye, Danny
c/o Rogers & Cowan
415 Madison Ave.
New York, NY 10022
entertainer

Kaye, Sammy
18 E. 48th St.
New York, NY 10017
entertainer

Kazan, Elia
850 7th Ave.
New York, NY 10019
producer, director, author

Kazan, Lainie
c/o Lainie & Company
9889 Santa Monica Blvd. #209
Beverly Hills, CA 90212
singer

Keaton, Diane
c/o Northrup
130 E. 67th St.
New York, NY 10021
actress

Keeler, Ruby
c/o Gloria Safier
667 Madison Ave.
New York, NY 10021
dancer

Keeshan, Bob
524 W. 57th St.
New York, NY 10019
"Captain Kangaroo"

Keith, Brian
P.O. Box 10025
Honolulu, HI 96816
actor

Keller, Marthe
c/o Maslansky-Koenigsberg
6671 Sunset Blvd. #1520A
Los Angeles, CA 90028
actress

Kellerman, Sally
c/o John Muiri
9200 Sunset Blvd.
Los Angeles, CA 90069
actress

Kelley, Clarence
c/o FBI
Washington DC 20535
former FBI director

Kelley, John
P.O. Box 124
Galeton, PA 16922
*organizer of woodsmen's
contest*

Kellogg Company
235 Porter St.
Battle Creek, MI 49016
J.E. Lonning, president

Kelly, Gene
c/o Chasin-Park-Citron
9255 Sunset Blvd.
Los Angeles, CA 90069
dancer, actor, director

Kemp, Jack F.
House Office Building
Washington DC 20515
U.S. representative

**Kemper Insurance
Company**
Kemper Insurance Building
Chicago, IL 60603
*James Scott Kemper,
president*

Kennedy, Arthur
c/o The Artists Agency
190 N. Canon Drive
Beverly Hills, CA 90210
actor

Kennedy, Caroline
1040 5th Ave.
New York, NY 10028
*daughter of
late John F. Kennedy*

Kennedy, David M.
U.S. Mission to NATO
1110 Brussels, Belgium
*former secretary
of the treasury*

**Kennedy, Edward
M. (Ted)**
Senate Office Building
Washington DC 20510
*senator from Massachusetts,
presidential candidate*

Kennedy, Ethel
Hickory Hill Mansion
1147 Chain Bridge Road
McLean, VA 22101
widow of Robert Kennedy

Kennedy, George
c/o Chasin-Park-Citron
9255 Sunset Blvd.
Los Angeles, CA 90069
actor

Kennedy, Joan
Squaw Island
Hyannisport, MA 02647
wife of Sen. Edward Kennedy

Kennedy, Rose
Hyannis, MA 02647
*mother of John, Robert and
Edward*

Kennerly, David
332 P St. NW
Washington DC 20007
*former White House photo-
grapher*

**Kentucky Fried
Chicken**
P.O. Box 13331
Louisville, KY 40213
Barry Rowles, president

Kermit the Frog
115 E. 57th St.
New York, NY 10022
muppet

Kerr, Dr. Clark
c/o Johnson Space Center
NASA
2101 Nasa Road
Houston, TX 77058
astronaut

Kerr, Deborah
c/o Wm. Morris
151 El Camino Drive
Beverly Hills, CA 90212
actress

Kerr, Graham
c/o Simon & Schuster
1230 Avenue of the Americas
New York, NY 10022
"The Galloping Gourmet"

Kerr, Jean
1 Beach Ave.
Larchmont, NY 10538
author

Kerr, Walter
230 W. 41st St.
New York, NY 10018
drama critic

Kerwin, Lance
c/o NBC TV
3000 W. Alameda Ave.
Burbank, CA 91505
actor

Ketcham, Hank
P.O. Box 800
Pebble Beach, CA 93953
cartoonist

Ketchum, Alton
Cos Cob, CT 06807
*owns world's largest
collection of old newspapers
(over 100,000)*

Key, Ted
1694 Glenhardie Road
Wayne, PA 19087
cartoonist

**Khaalis, Haamas
Abdul**
District of Columbia Jail
Washington DC 20004
terrorist

Khalid, King
Rujadh, Saudi Arabia
king of Saudi Arabia

Khambatta, Persis
c/o Bobbie Edrich
8957 Norma Place
Los Angeles, CA 90069
actress

Kheel, Theodore W.
280 Park Ave.
New York, NY 10017
labor mediator

**Khomeini, Ayatolla
Ruhollah**
Qom, Iran
*leader of Iran's
Islamic government*

Kidder, Margot
c/o Wm. Morris
151 El Camino Drive
Beverly Hills, CA 90212
actress

Kiley, Richard
c/o Stephen Draper
37 W. 57th St.
New York, NY 10019
actor

Killebrew, Harmon
P.O. Box 626
Ontario, OR 97914
former baseball player

Killy, Jean Claude
c/o International
Management
2 Erieview Plaza
Cleveland, OH 44114
skier

Kilpatrick, James
White Walnut Hill
Woodville, VA 22749
journalist

Kimberly, John
Route 1, Box 303
Queenstown, MD 21653
*retired paper
products manufacturer*

Kinal, Kathy
1830 Cherokee Ave.
Hollywood, CA 90028
*artist specializing in
decoration of Ukrainian eggs*

Kiner, Ralph
Thunderbird Ranch
Palm Springs, CA 92262
*member of baseball
Hall of Fame*

King, Alan
67 W. 55th St.
New York, NY 10019
entertainer

King, B.B.
c/o Promotions Consol, Inc.
3003 Airways #710
Memphis, TN 38131
singer, musician

King, Billie Jean
1660 S. Amphet Blvd. #266
San Mateo, CA 94402
tennis player

King, Bruce
Office of the Governor
Santa Fe, NM 87503
governor of New Mexico

King, Carole
P.O. Box 7308
Carmel, CA 93921
singer, songwriter

King, Coretta
234 Sunset Ave. NW
Atlanta, GA 30314
*widow of Martin Luther
King, Jr., lecturer*

King, Don
32 E. 69th St.
New York, NY 10021
boxing promoter

King, Edward J.
Office of the Governor
Boston, MA 02133
governor of Massachusetts

King, Woodie Jr.
417 Convent Ave.
New York, NY 10031
playwright

Kiplinger, Austin
1729 H St. NW
Washington DC 20006
publisher

Kirk, Claude R. Jr.
2937 Broadway
Riviera Beach, FL 33404
former governor of Florida

Kirkland, Lane
AFL-CIO
815 16th St. NW
Washington DC 20006
president, AFL-CIO

Kirshner, Don
9000 Sunset Blvd.
Los Angeles, CA 90069
producer, concert promoter

Kiss
c/o Aucoin Management Inc.
645 Madison Ave.
New York, NY 10022
music group

Kissinger, Henry
1800 K St. NW #520
Washington DC 20006
former secretary of state

Kitt, Eartha
c/o Henry Regnery Co.
180 N. Michigan Ave.
Chicago, IL 60601
actress, singer

Klassen, Elmer T.
7224 Arrowood Road
Bethesda, MD 20034
former postmaster general

Klein, Allen
1700 Broadway
New York, NY 10019
*former manager
of the Beatles*

Klein, Calvin
c/o Calvin Klein
205 W. 39th St.
New York, NY 10018
designer

Klein, Herbert G.
Metromedia, Inc.
5746 Sunset Blvd.
Los Angeles, CA 90028
former Nixon press official

Klein, Robert
c/o Rollins, Jaffe & Morra
130 W. 57th St.
New York, NY 10019
actor

**Kleindienst,
Richard G.**
c/o Colonial Mortgage
Corp. of DC
1101 17th St. NW
Washington DC 20036
former attorney general

Kleiner, Dick
1665 N. Beverly Drive
Beverly Hills, CA 90210
syndicated writer

Kloss, John
10 W. 66th St.
New York, NY 10023
designer

Klugman, Jack
c/o Diamond Artists
9200 Sunset Blvd. #909
Los Angeles, CA 90069
actor

Klutznik, Phillip
Dept. of Commerce
Washington DC 20230
secretary of commerce

Knauer, Virgina H.
Dept. of Health,
Education & Welfare
Washington DC 20201
consumer advocate

Knievel, Evel
P.O. Box 7777
Butte, MT 59701
stunt motorcyclist

Knight, Gladys
c/o Sidney Seidenberg
1414 Avenue of the Americas
New York, NY 10019
singer

Knight, Ted
c/o Ned N. Shankman
1888 Century Park E. #622
Los Angeles, CA 90067
actor

Knopf, Alfred
201 E. 50th St.
New York, NY 10028
publisher

Knotts, Don
c/o BNB Associates
9454 Wilshire Blvd. #309
Beverly Hills, CA 90212
actor

Koch, Edward I.
City Hall
New York, NY 10007
mayor of New York

Kodak Company
343 State St.
Rochester, NY 14650
Walter Fallon, president

Koehl, Matt
2507 N. Franklin Road
Arlington, VA 22205
*commander, National
Socialist White
People's Party*

Kohn, Roy
c/o George Cothran Flowers
238 E. 60th St.
New York, NY 10021
floral designer and teacher

Komack, James
c/o Warner Brothers
4000 Warner Blvd.
Burbank, CA 91522
producer

Korff, Rabbi Baruch
1221 Connecticut Ave. NW
Washington DC 20036
*former head of
Nixon Justice Fund*

Korman, Harvey
c/o Singer & Lewak
10960 Wilshire Blvd.
Los Angeles, CA 90024
actor

Kosinski, Jerzy
c/o Harcourt, Brace,
Jovanovich Inc.
757 3rd Ave.
New York, NY 10017
writer

Kosygin, Aleksei
Office of the Premier
Moscow, Soviet Union
*chairman, council of
ministers of Soviet Union*

Koufax, Sandy
R.R. 1, Box 79-A
Templeton, CA 93465
*member of baseball
Hall of Fame*

Krantz, Judith
c/o Crown
1 Park Ave.
New York, NY 10016
author

Kraus, Robert
201 Park Ave.
New York, NY 10010
cartoonist

Krebs, Ernest
1348 S. Van Ness Ave.
San Francisco, CA 94109
discoverer of Laetrile

Kristofferson, Kris
c/o Block-Kewley
Management
11 Bailey Ave.
Ridgefield, CT 06877
actor, singer, songwriter

Kroc, Ray
One McDonald Plaza
Oak Brook, IL 60521
*founder of McDonald's,
owner of San Diego Padres*

Krogh, Egil Jr.
c/o Swenson's Ice Cream Co.
333 Pine St.
San Francisco, CA 94104
former Nixon aide

Kubrick, Stanley
c/o Loeb & Loeb
10100 Santa Monica Blvd.
Los Angeles, CA 90067
producer

Kucinich, Dennis
12217 Milan
Cleveland, OH 44111
former Cleveland mayor

Kuhn, Bowie
Office of the Commissioner
75 Rockefeller Plaza
New York, NY 10019
baseball commissioner

Kulp, Nancy
5044 Laurel Canyon
N. Hollywood, CA 91607
actress

**Kunhardt,
Phillip B. Jr.**
c/o *Life Magazine*
Time-Life Building
Rockefeller Center
New York, NY 10020
managing editor

**Kunstler,
William M.**
Center for
Constitutional Rights
853 Broadway
New York, NY 10003
*attorney specializing
in controversial cases*

Kuralt, Charles
c/o CBS News
524 W. 57th St.
New York, NY 10019
journalist

Kuo-feng, Hua
Office of the Premier
Peking, China
premier of China

Labbe, Charles
P.O. Box 65
Ashton, R.I. 02864
leader, Amerian Nazi party

Ladd, Alan Jr.
4000 Warner Blvd.
Burbank, CA 91522
motion picture producer

Ladd, Cheryl
c/o Stone Associates
8489 W. 3rd St.
Los Angeles, CA 90048
actress

Laird, Melvin
c/o *Reader's Digest*
1730 Rhode Island Ave. NW
#212
Washington DC 20036
former secretary of defense

Lakein, Alan
2918 Webster St.
San Francisco, CA 94123
time-planning advisor

Laker, Sir Frederick
c/o Laker Airways
Gatwick Airport
Horley, Surrey
England
*airline executive, pioneer
of low-cost air travel*

Lamas, Fernando
9377 Readcrest Drive
Beverly Hills, CA 90210
actor, director

Lamm, Richard D.
Governor's Office
136 State Capitol
Denver, CO 80203
governor of Colorado

Lamparski, Richard
3289 Carse Canyon Drive
Hollywood, CA 90068
author

Lancaster, Burt
c/o ICM
8899 Beverly Blvd.
Los Angeles, CA 90048
actor

Lance, Bert
P.O. Box 637
Calhoun, GA 30701
*former director, Office of
Management and Budget*

Land, Edwin
549 Technology Square
Cambridge, MA 02139
*inventor of
Polaroid-Land camera*

Landau, Martin
1240 Benedict Canyon
Beverly Hills, CA 90210
actor

Lander, David
c/o ABC TV
4151 Prospect Ave.
Los Angeles, CA 90027
actor

Landers, Ann
c/o *Chicago Sun-Times*
401 N. Wabash Ave.
Chicago, IL 60611
columnist

Landon, Alf
P.O. Box 1280
Topeka, KS 66601
*former presidential
candidate*

Landon, Michael
c/o Paramount TV
5451 Marathon St.
Hollywood, CA 90038
*producer, director,
actor, writer*

**Landrieu,
Maurice "Moon"**
451 7th St. SW
Washington DC 20410
*secretary of housing
and urban development*

Landry, Tom
c/o Dallas Cowboys
6116 N. Central Expressway
Dallas, TX 75206
football coach

Lane, Abby
714 N. Beverly Drive
Beverly Hills, CA 90210
entertainer

Lane, Burton
146 Central Park W.
New York, NY 10023
composer

Lane, Mark
105 2nd St. NE
Washington DC 20002
*assassination conspiracy
advocate, author*

Lanin, Lester
Lester Lanin Orchestras
157 W. 57th St.
New York, NY 10019
orchestra leader

Langella, Frank
28 Woodhill Road
Wilton, CT 06897
actor

Lansbury, Angela
c/o Creative Artists Agency
1888 Century Park E.
#1400
Los Angeles, CA 90067
actress

Lansing, Sherry
c/o 20th Century Fox
10201 W. Pico Blvd.
Los Angeles, CA 90067
20th Century president;
first female studio head

Large Families of America
54 Miller St.
Fairfield, CT 06430
Judge John Henry
Norton, secretary

Larson, Don
17090 Cooper Hill Drive
Morgan Hill, CA 95037
former baseball player

Larson, Jack
449 Skyway Road N.
Los Angeles, CA 90049
played Jimmy Olsen
in "Superman" TV series

Larson, Nicolette
c/o Warner Brothers Records
3300 Warner Blvd.
Burbank, CA 91505
singer

Lasky, Victor
700 New Hampshire Ave. NW
Washington DC 20037
author

Lasley, Billy Lee
P.O. Box 551
San Diego, CA 92112
developer of captive
breeding programs for
endangered species of birds

Lasorda, Tommy
1000 Elysian Park Ave.
Los Angeles, CA 90012
baseball manager

Lassen, H.J.
Office of the Governor
Godthaab, Greenland
governor of Greenland

Lasser, Louise
c/o Pickwick
9744 Wilshire Blvd.
Beverly Hills, CA 90212
actress

Estee Lauder Inc.
767 5th Ave.
New York, NY 10022
cosmetics executive

Laufer, Charles
7060 Hollywood Blvd.
Hollywood, CA 90028
teen magazine publisher

Laughlin, Tom
12953 Marlboro
Los Angeles, CA 90068
actor, producer

Laver, Rod
c/o International
Management Group
1 Erieview Plaza
Cleveland, OH 44114
tennis player

Lavin, Linda
c/o CBS TV
7800 Beverly Blvd.
Los Angeles, CA 90036
actress

Lawford, Peter
c/o Gene Yusem
9000 Sunset Blvd. #502
Los Angeles, CA 90069
actor

Lawrence, Carol
c/o Wm. Morris
151 El Camino Drive
Beverly Hills, CA 90212
entertainer

Lawrence, Steve
c/o Stage 2
P.O. Box 5140
Beverly Hills, CA 90210
singer

Lawrence, Vickie
c/o Mark Mordoh
9200 Sunset Blvd. #905
Los Angeles, CA 90069
actress, singer

Laxalt, Paul
Senate Office Building
Washington DC 20510
senator from Nevada

Lazar, Irving "Swifty"
211 S. Beverly Drive
Beverly Hills, CA 90212
literary agent

Leachman, Cloris
c/o Creative Artists Agency
1888 Century Park E.
#1400
Los Angeles, CA 90067
actress

Learned, Michael
c/o Henderson/Hogan
Agency
247 S. Beverly Drive
Beverly Hills, CA 90212
actress

Leahy, Patrick J.
Senate Office Building
Washington DC 20510
senator from Vermont

Leary, Timothy L.
c/o Grove Press
55 E. 11th St.
New York, NY 10012
former LSD advocate

Le Carre, John
c/o Alfred Knopf
201 E. 50th St.
New York, NY 10022
author

Led Zeppelin
c/o Swan Song
444 Madison Ave.
New York, NY 10022
music group

Lee, Christopher
c/o Littman
409 N. Camden Drive #105
Beverly Hills, CA 90210
actor

Lee Jean Company
P.O. Box 1022
Reading, PA 19603
M.O. Lee, president

Lee, Peggy
1195 Tower Road
Beverly Hills, CA 90210
singer

Leek, Sybil
P.O. Box 158
Melbourne Beach, FL 32951
astrologer

Leffall, Dr. L. Jr.
Howard University Hospital
2041 Georgia Ave. NW
Washington DC 20060
general cancer surgeon

Lefkowitz, Louis J.
State Attorney General
The Capitol
Albany, NY 12201
government official

Lefrak, Samuel
97-77 Queens Blvd.
Forest Hills, NY 11374
housing corporation executive

Lehmam, Evelyn
111 E. 57th St.
New York, NY 10022
president, First Women's Bank

Leigh, Janet
c/o Creative Artists Agency
1888 Century Park E.
#1400
Los Angeles, CA 90067
actress

Lemmon, Jack
c/o Jalem Productions
141 El Camino Drive #201
Beverly Hills, CA 90212
actor

Lemon, Meadowlark
5746 Sunset Blvd.
Los Angeles, CA 90028
basketball player, actor

Lennon, John
c/o AVT Music
1370 Avenue of the Americas
New York, NY 10019
singer, songwriter

Leonard, Sheldon
315 S. Beverly Drive
Beverly Hills, CA 90212
producer

Leone, Mamma
c/o Mamma Leone's
Restaurant
239 W. 48th St.
New York, NY 10036
restaurateur

Lerner, Alan Jay
10 E. 40th St.
New York, NY 10016
lyricist

Leroy, Mervin
9200 Sunset Blvd.
Los Angeles, CA 90069
producer, director

Lessin, Dr. L.S.
George Washington
University Hospital
901 23rd St. NW
Washington DC 20037
*specialist in chemotherapy
and hermatology*

Lester, Richard
River Lane
Petersham
Surrey, England
director

Levene, Sam
St. Moritz Hotel
New York, NY 10019
actor

Levi Strauss Co.
2 Embarcadero Center
San Francisco, CA 94106
Walter Hass, Jr., president

Levi, Edward H.
c/o University of Chicago
1116 E. 59th St.
Chicago, IL 60637
*former attorney general;
former university president*

Levin, Carl
Senate Office Building
Washington DC 20510
senator from Michigan

Levine, Irving R.
4001 Nebraska Ave. NW
Washington DC 20016
news commentator

Levine, James
c/o Metropolitan Opera
Lincoln Center Plaza
New York, NY 10023
conductor

Levine, Joseph E.
345 Park Ave.
New York, NY 10022
producer

Levine, Michael
256 S. Robertson Blvd.
Beverly Hills, CA 90211
author

Levinson, Sam
156 Beach
147th St.
Neponsit, NY 11694
humorist

Levitt, Arthur
State Comptroller
State Office Building
Albany, NY 12207
government official

Lewis, Arthur D.
c/o American
Business Association
1025 Connecticut Ave. NW
Washington DC 20036
association president

Lewis, Jerry
1888 Century Park E. #830
Los Angeles, CA 90067
entertainer

Lewis, Jerry Lee
c/o Owens & Fain
1717 West End #322
Nashville, TN 37203
singer, musician

Liberace
c/o Seymour Heller
& Associates
9220 Sunset Blvd. #224
Los Angeles, CA 90069
pianist

Library of Congress
10 1st St. SE
Washington DC 20540
*Daniel Boorstin,
director*

Liddy, G. Gordon
9310 Ivanhoe Road
Oxon Hill, MD 20010
former Nixon aide

Lightfoot, Gordon
c/o EMP Ltd.
350 Davenport Road
Toronto, Ontario
Canada M5R 1K8
singer, songwriter

Lillie, Beatrice
25 East End Ave.
New York, NY 10028
actress

Lindberg, Ann Morrow
Scott's Cove
Darien, CT 06820
*author, widow of
Charles Lindberg*

Linden, Hal
c/o ICPR
9255 Sunset Blvd.
Los Angeles, CA 90069
actor, singer

Lindsay, John
1 W. 67th St.
New York, NY 10043
former mayor, author

Lindstrom, Pia
c/o CBS TV
524 W. 57th St.
New York, NY 10019
broadcast journalist

Link, Arthur
Office of the Governor
Bismark, ND 58505
governor of North Dakota

Linkletter, Art
8430 Wilshire Blvd.
Beverly Hills, CA 90211
television/radio host

List, Robert
Office of the Governor
Carson City, NV 89710
governor of Nevada

Little, Joanne
North Carolina Corrections
Center For Women
1034 Bragg St.
Raleigh, NC 27610
jail rape victim

Little, Rich
c/o Goldstein Co.
9200 Sunset Blvd. #913
Los Angeles, CA 90069
impressionist

Little League Baseball
Williamsport, PA 17701
Dr. Creighton Hale, president

Litton Industries
360 N. Crescent Drive
Beverly Hills, CA 90210
Charles Thornton, president

Lloyd, Chris Evert
1628 7th Place NE
Ft. Lauderdale, FL 33303
tennis player

Lloyd's of London
Lime St.
London EC3M 7HA
England
Sir H. Mance, president

Locke, Sandra
c/o Wm. Morris
151 El Camino Drive
Beverly Hills, CA 90212
actress

Lockhart, June
c/o Len Grant
P.O. Box 69360
Los Angeles, CA 90069
actress

Lockheed Aircraft
2555 N. Hollywood Way
Burbank, CA 91520
Robert Haack, chairman

Lodge, Henry Cabot
275 Hale St.
Beverly, MA 01915
author, former senator

Loeb, William
Manchester Union Leader
Manchester, NH 03105
publisher

Loengard, John
c/o *Life Magazine*
Time/Life Building
Rockefeller Center
New York, NY 10020
photo editor

Logan, Joshua
435 E. 52nd St.
New York, NY 10022
playwright, director

Loggins, Kenny
c/o Larry Larson
Associates Inc.
8732 Sunset Blvd. #600
Los Angeles, CA 90069
singer, songwriter

Long, Russell
Senate Office Building
Washington DC 20510
senator from Louisiana

Longet, Claudine
P.O. Box 3450
Aspen, CO 81611
singer

Longstreet, Robert
1137 Bass
Dunedin, FL 33528
organizer of Scottish Highland games

Lopez, Nancy
c/o Mark H.
McCormack Agency
1 Erieview Plaza
Cleveland, OH 44114
golfer

Lopez Portillo, Jose
Palacio Nacional
Mexico 1, DF
Mexico
president of Mexico

Lord, Jack
c/o Lord & Lady Enterprises
510 18th Ave.
Honolulu, HI 96818
actor

Lord, Mary Pillsbury
425 E. 58th St.
New York, NY 10022
civic worker

Loren, Sophia
Palazzo Colonna
Piazza d'Aracoeli
Rome, Italy
actress

Louis, Joe
3333 Seminole Circle
Las Vegas, NV 89109
*former heavyweight
champion*

**Lovelace, Linda
(Linda Boreman
Marciano)**
c/o Lyle Stuart Publishers
120 Enterprise
Secaucus, NJ 07094
actress

Lowery, Robert O.
c/o Bureau of Fire
Investigation
110 Church St.
New York, NY 10017
bureau commissioner

Loy, Myrna
c/o Kohner-Levy Agency
9169 Sunset Blvd.
Los Angeles, CA 90069
actress

Lucas, George
c/o 20th Century Fox
10201 Pico Blvd.
Los Angeles, CA 90064
producer, director

Luce, Claire Booth
4559 Kahala Ave.
Honolulu, HI 86816
*playwright, former
government official*

Luce, Henry III
Time-Life Building
New York, NY 10020
publisher

Lucey, Patrick S.
c/o American Embassy
P.O. Box 1471
Laredo, TX 78040
*U.S. ambassador
to Mexico*

Luciani, U. J.
P.O. Box 682
Cologne, NJ 08213
*author, Unusual
Contests In America*

**Luckash,
Dr. William**
The White House
1600 Pennsylvania Ave. NW
Washington DC 20500
*Jimmy Carter's
personal physician*

Luckman, Charles
9220 Sunset Blvd.
Los Angeles, CA 90069
architect

Ludden, Allan
11969 Ventura Blvd.
Studio City, CA 91604
producer, game show host

Ludlum, Robert
c/o Henry Morrison
58 W. 10th St.
New York, NY 10011
author

**Ludwig, Sister
Mary Paul**
Our Lady of Mercy
Catholic Church
Duluth, MN 55802
*America's only female
Catholic pastor*

Lugar, Richard G.
Senate Office Building
Washington DC 20510
senator from Indiana

Lumet, Sidney
c/o ICM
8899 Beverly Blvd.
Los Angeles, CA 90048
director

Lupino, Ida
c/o Goldin-Dennis-Karg
470 S. San Vicente Blvd.
Los Angeles, CA 90048
actress, director

Lynch, John
Taoiseach Office
Dublin, Ireland
prime minister of Ireland

Lynde, Paul
P.O. Box 69640
Los Angeles, CA 90048
comedian

Lynn, Fred
12040 Klingerman St.
El Monte, CA 91732
baseball player

Lynn, James T.
6736 Newbold Drive
Bethesda, MD 20034
*former official, Office
of Management and Budget*

Lynn, Janet
c/o Ice Follies
1600 Dain Tower
Minneapolis, MN 55402
figure skater

Lynn, Loretta
1511 Sigler St.
Nashville, TN 37203
singer

Lyon, Phyllis
1523 Franklin St.
San Francisco, CA 94109
*director, National Sex
Forum Organization*

Maazel, Lorin
Cleveland Orchestra
Severance Hall
Cleveland, OH 44106
conductor

Maas, Peter
c/o Sterling Lord Agency
660 Madison Ave.
New York, NY 10021
writer

MacFarland, Spanky
Route 3, Box 106
Smithfield, TX 70680
former star of "Little Rascals"

MacGraw, Ali
c/o ICM
8899 Beverly Blvd.
Los Angeles, CA 90048
actress

MacGregor, Clark
United Technologies Corp.
1125 15th St. NW
Washington DC 20005
former Nixon campaign director

MacGuire, Andrew
House Office Building
Washington DC 20515
U.S. representative

Mack Truck Company
2100 Mack Blvd.
Allentown, PA 18105
A.W. Pelletier, president

Mackie, Bob
8636 Melrose Ave.
Los Angeles, CA 90069
designer

MacLaine, Shirley
c/o Chasin-Park-Citron
9255 Sunset Blvd.
Los Angeles, CA 90069
entertainer, actress

MacMurray, Fred
c/o Chasin-Park-Citron
9255 Sunset Blvd.
Los Angeles, CA 90069
actor

MacNelley, Jeffrey
333 E. Grace St.
Richmond, VA 23219
cartoonist

MacPhail, Leland
280 Park Ave.
New York, NY 10017
president, baseball's American League

MacRae, Carmen
2200 Summitridge Drive
Beverly Hills, CA 90210
singer

Macy's Department Store
151 W. 34th St.
New York, NY 10001
Donald Smiley, president

Maddox, Elliott
250 W. 57th St.
New York, NY 10019
baseball player

Maddox, Lester G.
Mount Paran Road
Atlanta, GA 30338
former governor of Georgia

Magnuson, Warren G.
Senate Office Building
Washington DC 20510
senator from Washington

Magruder, Jeb S.
c/o Young Life
P.O. Box 520
Colorado Springs, CO 80901
former Nixon aide

Magyar, Gabriel
708 Dover Place
Champaign, IL 61820
cellist

Maheu, Robert A.
c/o Leisure Industries
P.O. Box 11068
Las Vegas, NV 89101
former Howard Hughes aide

Mahoney, James
1036 College St.
Saskatoon, Sk.
Canada SK S7N OW1
Roman Catholic bishop

Maier, Henry W.
City Hall
Milwaukee, WI 53202
mayor of Milwaukee

Mailer, Norman
P.O. Box 338
Provincetown, MA 02657
author

**Major League
Umpires Association**
450 W. 14th St.
Chicago Heights, IL 60411
William Williams, director

Majors, Lee
c/o Jay Bernstein
9110 Sunset Blvd.
Los Angeles, CA 90069
actor

Makarova, Natalia
c/o American Ballet Theatre
888 7th Ave.
New York, NY 10019
ballerina

Malden, Karl
c/o Wm. Morris
151 El Camino Drive
Beverly Hills, CA 90212
actor

Malone, Dorothy
c/o Contemporary-Korman
Artists
132 Lasky Drive
Beverly Hills, CA 90212
actress

Man Watchers Inc.
2865 State St.
San Diego, CA 92103
Suzy Mallery, president

Manchester, Melissa
c/o Rollis, Joffe, et al.
130 W. 57th St.
New York, NY 10019
singer, songwriter

Manchester, William
c/o Harold Maston Co.
22 E. 40th St.
New York, NY 10016
author

Mancini, Henry
c/o Regency Artists
9200 Sunset Blvd. #823
Los Angeles, CA 90069
composer, conductor

Mandel, Marvin
c/o Frank A. DeFilippo
Cross Keyes Road
Baltimore, MD 21210
suspended governor

Mangione, Chuck
c/o Gates Music
270 Midtown Plaza
Rochester, NY 14604
musician, composer

Manilow, Barry
c/o Miles Lourie
314 W. 71st St.
New York, NY 10023
singer, songwriter

Mann, Herbie
985 5th Ave.
New York, NY 10021
musician

Mansfield, Mike
U.S. State Department
Washington DC 20520
*former Senate majority
leader, ambassador to Japan*

Manson, Charles
California Medical Facility
Vacaville, CA 95688
*convicted mass murderer;
cult leader*

Mantle, Mickey
5730 Watson Circle
Dallas, TX 75225
*member of baseball
Hall of Fame*

Maravich, Pete
c/o New Orleans
Jazz Superdome
Box 53213
New Orleans, LA 70153
basketball player

Maraziti, Joseph J.
Maraziti, Maraziti & Corra
117 Cornelia St.
Boonton, NJ 07005
former congressman

Marceau, Marcel
c/o Columbia Artists
165 W. 57th St.
New York, NY 10019
mime

Marchetti, Victor L.
265 Lafayette St.
New York, NY 10013
former CIA agent

Marcus, Stanley
800 Republic National Bank
Dallas, TX 75201
*etail executive
(Neiman-Marcus)*

Mardian, Robert C.
323 N. Central Ave.
Phoenix, AZ 22101
ttorney

Maris, Roger
Maris Distribution Co.
Gainesville, FL 32601
*ecord for most home runs
n one season — 61*

Marks, Albert J.
325 Broadway
Atlantic City, NJ 08401
*irector, Miss
America Pageant*

Markey, Howard K.
U.S. Court of Custom
& Patent Appeals
Washington DC 20439
*hief judge, U.S. Court of
Customs & Patent Appeals*

Markey, Lucille
Calumet Farms
Lexington, KY 40505
horoughbred breeder

Marley, John
c/o ICM
899 Beverly Blvd.
Los Angeles, CA 90048
ctor

Marriott Hotels
5161 River Road
Washington DC 20016
John Marriott, president

Marshack, Megan
25 W. 54th St.
New York, NY 10019
*aide to Nelson Rockefeller,
present at his death*

Marshall, Penny
c/o Creative Artists Agency
1888 Century Park E. #1400
Los Angeles, CA 90067
actress

Marshall, E.G.
Bryan Lake Road RFD #2
Mt. Keoco, NY 10549
actor

Marshall, Peter
c/o Wm. Morris
151 El Camino Drive
Beverly Hills, CA 90212
game show host

Marshall, Ray
Department of Labor
Washington DC 20210
secretary of labor

Marshall, Robert
231 Madison Ave.
New York, NY 10016
*president, Lutheran
Church of America*

Marshall, Thurgood
U.S. Supreme Court
Washington DC 20543
justice

Martin, Billy
c/o New York Yankees
Yankee Stadium
Bronx, NY 10451
baseball manager

Martin, Dean
c/o Chase-Park-Citron
9255 Sunset Blvd.
Los Angeles, CA 90069
actor, entertainer

Martin, Graham A.
c/o Retirement Division
PER/ES/RET, Rm. 1251,
New State
Washington DC 20520
*former ambassador
to Viet Nam*

Martin, Mary
364 Veredanore
Palm Springs, CA 92262
actress

Martin, Pamela Sue
c/o Wm. Morris
151 El Camino Drive
Beverly Hills, CA 90212
actress

Martin, Quinn
c/o Quinn Martin
Productions
1041 Formosa Ave.
Los Angeles, CA 90046
producer

Martin, Steve
P.O. Box 3438
Aspen, CO 81611
entertainer

Martinez, Eugenio R.
c/o Daniel E. Schultz
1990 M St. NW #510
Washington DC 20036
convicted Watergate burglar

Marvin, Lee
c/o Mishkin Agency
9255 Sunset Blvd.
Los Angeles, CA 90069
actor

Marvin, Michelle Triola
c/o Marvin Mitchelson
1801 Century Park E. #1900
Los Angeles, CA 90067
principle in landmark "palimony" decision

Mary Kay Cosmetics
8900 Carpentar Freeway
Dallas, TX 75247
Mary Kay Ash, president

Mason, James
Maggie Park
55 Park Lane
London, W1 England
actor

Mason, Marsha
c/o Wm. Morris
151 El Camino Drive
Beverly Hills, CA 90212
actress

Massey, Raymond
913 N. Beverly Drive
Beverly Hills, CA 90210
actor

Master Charge
Interbank
888 7th Ave.
New York, NY 10019
John Reynolds, president

Masters, William
2221 S. Warson Road
St. Louis, MO 63124
sex therapist

Matheny, Danny
P.O. Box 3663
Little Rock, AR 72203
organizer of 120-mile explorer canoe race

Matheson, Scott M.
Office of the Governor
Salt Lake City, UT 84114
governor of Utah

Matheson, Tim
c/o L. Frank & Co.
1801 Avenue of the Stars
Los Angeles, CA 90067
actor

Mathias, Charles M. Jr.
Senate Office Building
Washington DC 20510
senator from Maryland

Mathis, Johnny
c/o Rojon Productions
6290 Sunset Blvd. #1701
Hollywood, CA 90028
singer

Matsunaga, Spark M.
Senate Office Building
Washington DC 20510
senator from Hawaii

Matthau, Walter
10100 Santa Monica Blvd. #2200
Los Angeles, CA 90067
actor

Mauch, Gene
c/o Minnesota Twins
8001 Cedar Ave.
Bloomington, MN 55428
baseball manager

Mauldin, William
c/o *Chicago Sun-Times*
401 N. Wabash Ave.
Chicago, IL 60611
cartoonist

Max Factor Co.
1655 N. McCadden Place
Hollywood, CA 90028
Samuel Kalish, president

Max, Peter
11 Riverside Drive
New York, NY 10023
artist

May, Elaine
320 W. 81st St.
New York, NY 10023
director, writer, comedienne

Mayer, Jean
c/o Tufts University
Ballou Hall
Medford, MA 02155
scientist

Oscar Mayer Meat Company
P.O. Box 7188
Madison, WI 53707
P. Goff Beach, president

Mayflower Moving Co.
9998 N. Michigan Road
Carmel, IN 46032
E.J. Grumme, president

Mays, Willie
51 Mt. Vernon
Atherton, CA 94025
*member of baseball
Hall of Fame*

Mazursky, Paul
c/o ICM
8899 Beverly Blvd.
Los Angeles, CA 90048
director, writer

McAdoo, Bob
c/o New York Knicks
5 Pennsylvania Plaza
New York, NY 10001
basketball player

McBride, Dr. C.
M.D. Anderson Hospital
& Tumor Institute
6723 Bertner Drive
Houston, TX 77030
*surgeon specializing in
breast surgery & melanoma*

McBride, Lloyd
United Steelworkers
of America
5 Gateway Center
Pittsburgh, PA 15222
union president

McBride, Patricia
c/o New York City Ballet
Lincoln Center for the
Performing Arts
New York, NY 10023
ballerina

McCall Pattern Co.
230 Park Ave.
New York, NY 10017
*Earle K. Angstadt Jr.,
president*

McCambridge, Mercedes
c/o Hussong Agency
9000 Sunset Blvd.
Los Angeles, CA 90069
actress

McCarthy, Eugene
1420 N St. NW
Washington DC 90069
writer, former senator

McCartney, Paul
c/o McCartney
Productions Ltd.
12-13 Greek St.
London, W1 England
singer, songwriter

McCloskey, Paul N. Jr.
House Office Building
Washington DC 20515
U.S. representative

McCloskey, Robert J.
Department of State
Washington DC 20520
*ambassador to
The Netherlands*

McClure, Doug
P.O. Box 1145
Pebble Beach, CA 93953
actor

McClure, James A.
Senate Office Building
Washington DC 20510
senator from Idaho

McConnell, M.J.
4716 Vineland
N. Hollywood, CA 91602
*world's foremost
barter expert*

McCoo, Marilyn
c/o Dick Broder
Personal Mgmt.
9151 Sunset Blvd.
Los Angeles, CA 90069
singer

McCord, James
c/o William A. Mann
4700 Authority Place
Camp Springs, MD 20031
convicted Watergate burglar

McCormack, John W.
111 Perkins St.
Jamaica Plains
Boston, MA 02130
former congressman

McDonald, Ronald
1 McDonald Plaza
Oak Brook, IL 60521
mascot

McDonald's Corp.
1 McDonald Plaza
Oak Brook, IL 60521
*Ray Kroc, founder
and chairman*

McDowall, Roddy
c/o Wm. Morris
151 El Camino Drive
Beverly Hills, CA 90212
actor

McDowell, Frank
Alexander Young Blvd.
Honolulu, HI 96813
plastic surgeon

McEnroe, John
c/o Paul, Weiss, Rifkind
345 Park Ave.
New York, NY 10022
tennis player

McGoon, Dr. D.C.
Mayo Clinic
Rochester, MN 55901
heart surgeon

McGovern, George
Senate Office Building
Washington DC 20510
senator from South Dakota

McGrary, Billy & Benny
Hendersonville, NC 28739
*world's heaviest
twins (740 lbs. each)*

McGraw-Hill Co.
1221 Avenue of the Americas
New York, NY 10020
*Harold W. McGraw,
president*

McGree, Dean
c/o Kerr-McGree Center
Oklahoma City, OK 73125
oil company executive

McGregor, Maurice
c/o Royal Victoria Hospital
687 Pine Ave.
Montreal, PQ Canada
cardiologist

McGrory, Mary
c/o Washington State
225 Virginia Ave. SE
Washington DC 20061
writer

McHenry, Donald
U.S. Mission to
the United Nations
799 U.N. Plaza
New York, NY 10017
*U.S. ambassador
to United Nations*

McIntyre, James
Office of Management
& Budget
Executive Office Building
Washington DC 20503
director, Office of the Budget

McKay, Jim
c/o ABC Sports
1330 Avenue of the Americas
New York, NY 10019
sports commentator

McKay, John
c/o Tampa Bay Buccaneers
1 Buccaneer Plaza
Tampa, FL 33607
football coach

McKean, Michael
c/o ABC TV
4151 Prospect Ave.
Los Angeles, CA 90027
actor

McKuen, Rod
P.O. Box G
Beverly Hills, CA 90213
poet

McMahon, Ed
c/o NBC TV
3000 W. Alameda Ave.
Burbank, CA 91505
entertainer

McManaway, James
5505 Center St.
Chevy Chase, MD 20015
Shakespearian scholar

McNair, Barbara
c/o Moss Agency
113 N. San Vicente Blvd.
Beverly Hills, CA 90211
singer

McNair, Robert E.
P.O. Box 11895
Columbia, SC 29211
former governor

McNally, Terrence
218 W. 10th St.
New York, NY 10014
playwright

McNamara, Robert
2412 Tracy Place
Washington DC 20008
president, World Bank;
former secretary of defense

McNichol, Jimmy
c/o Goldberg-Ehrlich
9701 Wilshire Blvd. #800
Beverly Hills, CA 90212
actor

McNichol, Kristy
c/o Goldberg-Ehrlich
9701 Wilshire Blvd. #800
Beverly Hills, CA 90212
actress

McQueen, Steve
c/o Rogers & Cowan
9665 Wilshire Blvd.
Beverly Hills, CA 90212
actor

Meade, Julia
1010 5th Ave.
New York, NY 10028
actress

Meadows, Audrey
c/o Val Spring Associates
527 Madison Ave.
New York, NY 10022
actress

Meadows, Jayne
16185 Woodvale
Encino, CA 91316
actress

Means, Russell
c/o American
Indian Movement
P.O. Box 3677
St. Paul, MN 55101
movement leader

Meara, Anne
c/o Janice Morgan
Communications
250 W. 57th St.
New York, NY 10019
comedienne

**Meat Loaf
(Marvin Lee Aday)**
c/o ICM
8899 Beverly Blvd.
Los Angeles, CA 90048
singer

Melcher, John
Senate Office Building
Washington DC 20510
senator from Montana

Medina, Frank
6553 E. Waterloo Road
Stockton, CA 95205
collector of
antique windmills

**Meeropol, Mike
& Robert**
c/o Houghton Mifflin Co.
2 Park St.
Boston, MA 02107
sons of Ethel &
Julius Rosenberg

Mehta, Zubin
c/o New York Philharmonic
Avery Fisher Hall
Broadway and 65th St.
New York, NY 10023
conductor

Mellon, Paul
1729 H St. NW
Washington DC 20006
art gallery executive

Melnick, Daniel
300 Colgems Square
Burbank, CA 91505
studio executive

Menninger, Karl
Menninger Foundation
P.O. Box 829
Topeka, KS 66601
psychiatrist

Menuhin, Yehudi
c/o Columbia Artists Mgmt.
165 W. 57th St.
New York, NY 10019
violinist

Mercer, Mabel
P.O. Box 781
East Chatham, NY 12060
singer

Mercouri, Melina
c/o Wm. Morris
1350 Avenue of the Americas
New York, NY 10019
actress

Meredith, Burgess
c/o Jack Fields
9225 Sunset Blvd. #1001
Los Angeles, CA 90069
actor

Meredith, Don
Meredith Productions
1004 Summit Drive
Beverly Hills, CA 90210
sports commentator, actor

Meredith, Scott
845 3rd Ave.
New York, NY 10022
literary agent

Meriwether, Lee
c/o Levin & Associates
328 S. Beverly Drive #E
Beverly Hills, CA 90212
actress

Merman, Ethel
c/o Lionel Larner
850 7th Ave.
New York, NY 10019
singer, actress

Merrick, David
246 W. 44th St.
New York, NY 10036
producer

Metzenbaum, Howard
Senate Office Building
Washington DC 20510
senator from Ohio

Meyer, Eugene
946 Ohayo Mt. Road
Woodstock, NY 12498
chess player

Meyer, Russell
Highlands Clinic Building
Williamson, WV 25661
neurologist, neurosurgeon

Meyerhoff, Joseph
25 S. Charles St.
Baltimore, MD 21021
philanthropist

Michaels, Lorne
c/o NBC TV
30 Rockefeller Plaza
New York, NY 10020
producer

Michener, James
P.O. Box 125
Pipersville, PA 18947
author

Middendorf, J. William Jr.
Office of the Secretary
of the Navy
Washington DC 20350
secretary of the navy

Merrill, Dina
c/o Eve Siegal
35 W. 53rd St.
New York, NY 10019
actress

Merrill, Lynch, Pierce, Fenner & Smith
1 Liberty Plaza
165 Broadway
New York, NY 10006
Donald T. Regan, president

Merrill, Robert
c/o Metropolitan Opera
Lincoln Center
New York, NY 10023
singer

Meshill, Thomas
84 Randeckers Lane
Kensington, CT 06037
judge, former congressman

Messina, Jim
c/o Larry Larson Associates
8723 Sunset Blvd. #600
Los Angeles, CA 90069
singer

Metro-Goldwyn-Mayer
10202 Washington Blvd.
Culver City, CA 90230
David Begelman, president

Metropolitan Life Insurance Company
1 Madison Ave
New York, NY 10010
Richard R. Shinn, president

Midler, Bette
c/o Miss M Productions
Burbank Studios
Burbank, CA 91505
singer, actress

Mike, Takeu
Office of the Prime Minister
Tokyo, Japan
prime minister of Japan

Mikita, Stan
1840 W. Madison St.
Chicago, IL 60612
hockey player

Miles, Sarah
c/o ICM
8899 Beverly Blvd.
Los Angeles, CA 90048
actress

Miles, Tichi Wilkerson
c/o *The Hollywood Reporter*
6715 Sunset Blvd.
Hollywood, CA 90028
publisher

Miles, Vera
c/o Mark Levin Associates
328 S. Beverly Drive #E
Beverly Hills, CA 90212
actress

Milland, Ray
c/o Contemporary-Korman
Artists
132 Lasky Drive
Beverly Hills, CA 90212
actor

Miller, Ann
c/o Contemporary-Korman
Artists
132 Lasky Drive
Beverly Hills, CA 90212
actress, dancer

Miller, Arnold
900 15th St. NW
Washington DC 20005
president, United Mine Workers

Miller, Arthur
1109 S. Main St.
Kokomo, IN 46902
steel company executive

Miller, Arthur
c/o ICM
40 W. 57th St.
New York, NY 10019
playwright, author

Miller, G. William
15th St. &
Pennsylvania Ave. NW
Washington DC 20220
secretary of the treasury

Miller, Herbert J. Jr.
1150 Connecticut Ave. NW
#1000
Washington DC 20036
former federal affairs counselor

Miller, John
451 Russell Lane
Suffield, CT 06078
actuary

Miller, Johnny
10880 Wilshire Blvd. #1800
Los Angeles, CA 90024
golfer

Miller, Karl Lewis
P.O. Box 824
Arleta, CA 91331
animal trainer and director

Miller, Linda
890 Broadway
New York, NY 10003
ballerina

Miller, Marvin
375 Park Ave.
New York, NY 10022
president, Baseball Players Association

Millet, Kate
Box D
Billings, MT 12510
feminist

Milliken, William G.
Office of the Governor
State Capitol Building
Lansing, MI 48933
governor of Michigan

Mills, Wilbur D.
1600 S. Eads
Arlington, VA 22202
former congressman

Mimieux, Yvette
300 Stone Canyon Road
Los Angeles, CA 90024
actress

Minguy, Claude
8173 Zoo Ave.
Charlesbourg, PQ, Canada
zoo director

Mink, Patsy
U.S. State Department
Washington DC 20520
*ass't secretary for oceans &
international environmental
& scientific affairs*

Minnelli, Liza
c/o Ufland Agency
190 N. Canon Drive #200
Beverly Hills, CA 90210
actress, entertainer

Minnelli, Vincente
812 N. Crescent Drive
Beverly Hills, CA 90210
director

Miranda, Vincent
5445 Sunset Blvd.
Hollywood, CA 90027
*president of Pussycat
Theatres, country's largest
chain of x-rated theatres*

Mirisch, Walter
c/o Universal Studios
100 Universal City Plaza
Universal City, CA 91608
producer

**Mistresses
Anonymous**
P.O. Box 2
Massapequa, NY 11758
Melissa Sands, president

Mitchell, John
1030 5th Ave.
New York, NY 10028
*former attorney-general,
convicted Watergate
conspirator*

Mitchell, Joni
c/o Lookout Management
9120 Sunset Blvd.
Los Angeles, CA 90069
singer, songwriter

Mitchelson, Marvin
1801 Century Park E.
#1900
Los Angeles, CA 90067
attorney

Mitchum, Robert
c/o Talbot Productions
9229 Sunset Blvd.
Los Angeles, CA 90069
actor

**Mobil Oil
Corporation**
150 E. 42nd St.
New York, NY 10017
*Rawleigh Warner Jr.,
chairman*

Moffo, Anna
c/o Edgar Vincent
Associates
156 E. 52nd St.
New York, NY 10022
singer

Mondale, Walter F.
Old Executive Office Building
Washington DC 20501
vice-president

Money, Eddie
201 11th St.
San Francisco, CA 94103
singer

Monroe, Earl
c/o New York Knicks
4 Pennsylvania Plaza
New York, NY 10001
basketball player

Monster, Cookie
c/o Children's
Television Workshop
1 Lincoln Plaza
New York, NY 10023
"Sesame Street" character

Montagu, Ashley
321 Cherry Hill Road
Princeton, NJ 08540
anthropologist

Montalban, Ricardo
c/o Contemporary-Korman
Artists
132 Lasky Drive
Beverly Hills, CA 90212
actor

**Montgomery,
Elizabeth**
c/o Wm. Morris
151 El Camino Drive
Beverly Hills, CA 90212
actress

Montgomery-Ward
Montgomery-Ward Plaza
Chicago, IL 60671
*Edward S. Donnell,
president*

Montoya, Carlos
345 W. 58th St.
New York, NY 10019
guitarist

Montoya, Joseph M.
11 E. San Francisco
Santa Fe, NM 87501
former senator

Moody's Investor Service
99 Church St.
New York, NY 10007
John Brenner, president

Moon, Sun Myung
Unification Church
4 W. 43rd St.
New York, NY 10036
religious leader

Moore, Arch A. Jr.
507 Jefferson Ave.
Glen Dale, WV 26038
former governor

Moore, Clayton
4720 Parkolivo
Calabasas, CA 91302
actor — "Lone Ranger"

Moore, Dudley
c/o ICM
8899 Beverly Blvd.
Los Angeles, CA 90048
actor, pianist

Moore, Gary
430 Park Ave.
New York, NY 10022
television host

Moore, Mary Tyler
c/o MTM Productions
4024 Radford Ave.
Studio City, CA 91604
actress

Moore, Melba
c/o Wm. Morris
1350 Avenue of the Americas
New York, NY 10018
singer, actress

Moore, Roger
c/o Chasin-Park-Citron
9255 Sunset Blvd.
Los Angeles, CA 90069
actor

Moore, Sara Jane
Women's Federal Prison
P.O. Box W
Alderson, WV 24910
would-be assassin of Gerald Ford

Moore, William H.
11012 Stanmore Drive
Potomac, MD 20854
retired president of Penn Central Railroad

Moorer, Thomas H.
The Pentagon
Washington DC 20301
former chairman, Joint Chiefs of Staff

Morath, Max
850 7th Ave.
New York, NY 10019
ragtime entertainer

Morgan, Jaye P.
c/o Carman Productions Inc.
15456 Cabrito Road
Van Nuys, CA 91409
entertainer

Morgan, Robert B.
Senate Office Building
Washington DC 20510
senator from North Carolina

Morgan, William
Yerkes Observatory
Williams Bays, WI 53191
astronomer

Moriarty, Michael
c/o Smith-Stevens
1650 Broadway
New York, NY 10019
actor

Morris, William Jr.
c/o Wm. Morris
151 El Camino Drive
Beverly Hills, CA 90212
talent agent

Morrison, Van
c/o Robert Gordon
555 California St. #3100
San Francisco, CA 94104
singer, songwriter

Morse, Joseph
c/o Charter New York Corp.
1 Wall St.
New York, NY 10005
financier

Morton, Dr. D.L.
UCLA
10833 Le Conte Ave.
Los Angeles, CA 90024
surgeon specializing in melanoma and sarcoma

Morton, Rogers C.B.
Rt. 1
Easton, MD 21601
former secretary of commerce and secretary of interior

Moses, Robert
c/o Randall's Island
P.O. Box 35
New York, NY 10035
park developer

Moss, Frank E.
1848 S. Wasatch Drive
Salt Lake City, UT 84108
former senator

Moss, Geoffrey
315 E. 68th St.
New York, NY 10021
cartoonist

Moss, Jerry
c/o A&M Records
1416 N. La Brea Ave.
Hollywood, CA 90028
co-founder, A&M Records

Most, Donny
c/o L. Frank & Co.
1801 Avenue of the Stars
Los Angeles, CA 90067
actor

Mothers-in-Law Club International
739 Chestnut St.
Cedarhurst, Long Island
NY 11516
Sylvia Parker, president

Motorola Company
1303 E. Algonquin Road
Schammberg, IL 60196
Robert Galvin, president

Mott, Stewart
515 Madison Ave.
New York, NY 10022
political activist

Mouse, Mickey
500 S. Buena Vista St.
Burbank, CA 91521
cartoon character

Moyers, Bill
c/o CBS TV
524 W. 57th St.
New York, NY 10019
journalist, former presidential press secretary

Moynihan, Daniel
Senate Office Building
Washington DC 20510
senator from New York

Mudd, Roger
2020 M St.
Washington DC 20036
journalist

Muhammad, Wallace
4855 S. Woodlawn
Chicago, IL. 60615
religious leader

Mull, Martin
c/o Charles Joffe
Universal Studios
Universal City, CA 91608
comedian

Mulligan, Richard
c/o ABC TV
4151 Prospect Ave.
Los Angeles, CA 90027
actor

Mumalo, G.
15 Konley Drive
Kalispell, MT 59901
organizer of canoe races

Murcer, Bobby
c/o New York Yankees
Yankee Stadium
Bronx, NY 10451
baseball player

Murdoch, Rupert
210 South St.
New York, NY 10022
publisher

Murphy, Melvin "Turk"
729 Chestnut St.
San Francisco, CA 94111
trombonist

Murphy, Reg
c/o *San Francisco Examiner*
110 5th St.
San Francisco, CA 94119
publisher

Murray, Anne
1750 N. Vine St.
Hollywood, CA 90028
singer

Murray, Jean Shaw
2620 P St.
Washington DC 20007
*publisher, Green Book
(Washington social register)*

Musial, Stan
85 Trent Drive
La Due, MO 63124
*member of baseball
Hall of Fame*

Muskie, Edmund
Senate Office Building
Washington DC 20510
senator from Maine

Musselman, Mike
Roy, UT 84067
*world doughnut-eating
champion (27 in 7 minutes)*

**Mutual of Omaha
Insurance**
Dodge at 33rd St.
Omaha, NE 68131
V.J. Skutt, president

Myerson, Bess
220 E. 42nd St.
New York, NY 10017
consumer advocate

Nabors, Jim
c/o Wm. Morris
151 El Camino Drive
Beverly Hills, CA 90212
actor, singer

Nader, Ralph
P.O. Box 19367
Washington DC 20034
consumer advocate, attorney, author

Namath, Joe
c/o James Walsh
450 Park Ave. #1500
New York, NY 10022
actor, retired football player

Name That Tune
1717 N. Highland Ave.
Hollywood, CA 90028
Joanna Cooper, talent coordinator

Nash, Graham
c/o Professional Management
511 W. Alabama St. #201
Houston, TX 77006
singer, songwriter

Nassikas, John N.
21 DuPont Circle NW
Washington DC 20036
former chairman, Federal Power Commission; member, National Petroleum Council

Nastase, Ilie
c/o Mitch Oprea
107 W. 75th St. Apt. 2A
New York, NY 10023
tennis player

Nathan's Famous Restaurant
1515 Broadway
New York, NY 10036
Murray Handwerker, president

National Aeronautics and Space Administration
400 Maryland Ave. SW
Washington DC 20546
Robert A. Frosch, administrator

National Airlines
P.O. Box 592055
Miami, FL 33159
Lewis Maytag, president

National Association of Basketball Referees
3 Grand Plaza
Philadelphia, PA 19102
Darell Garretson, director

National Broadcasting Co.
30 Rockefeller Plaza
New York, NY 10020
Julian Goodman, president

National Clean Air Association
620 C St. SE
Washington DC 20003
Richard Ayres, director

National Coalition Against the Death Penalty
22 E. 40th St.
New York, NY 10016
Henry Schwarzschild, executive director

National Committee to Ban Handguns
100 Maryland Ave. NE
Washington, DC 20002
Michael K. Beard, director

National Council of Young Men's Christian Associations
291 Broadway
New York, NY 10007
Dr. Robert W. Harlan, executive director

National Council on Alcoholism
733 3rd Ave.
New York, NY 10017
George C. Dimas, executive director

National Council on Drug Abuse
8 S. Michigan Ave.
Chicago, IL 60603
Dr. Jordan Scher, director

National Easter Seal Society
2023 W. Ogden Ave.
Chicago, IL 60612
John L. Garrison, executive director

National Enquirer
Lantana, FL 33460
Generoso Pope Jr., publisher

National Family Planning Council
7060 Hollywood Blvd.
Suite 414
Los Angeles, CA 90028
*Kenneth I. Allen,
executive director*

National Gay Task Force
80 5th Ave.
New York, NY 10011
S. Endean, chairperson

National Jogging Association
919 18th St. NW
Suite 830
Washington DC 20006
Gary K. Olsen, director

National Labor Board
1717 Pennsylvania Ave. NW
Washington DC 20570
John H. Fanning, chairman

National Association to Aid Fat Americans
P.O. Box 43
Bellrose, NY 11426
*Lisbeth Fisher,
executive secretary*

National Right to Life Commitee
557 National Press Bldg.
529 14th St. NW
Washington DC 20045
*Judie Brown, public
relations director*

National Society for the Preservation of Covered Bridges
Federal St.
Beverly, MA 01915
Roger D. Griffin, president

National Wheelchair Athletic Association
40-24 62nd St.
Woodside, NY 11377
Benjamin Lipton, director

Navratilova, Martina
c/o Pro Sports Management
16211 Spring Creek Road
Dallas, TX 75248
tennis player

Nederlander, James
1564 Broadway
New York, NY 10036
theatre executive

Neff, Francine
1509 Sagebrush Trail SE
Albuquerque, NM 87123
former U.S. treasurer

Negri, Pola
7707 Broadway
San Antonio, TX 78209
*silent screen actress, engaged
to Rudolph Valentino at the
time of his death*

Neill, Noel
P.O. Box 1370
Studio City, CA 91604
*Lois Lane in "Superman" TV
series*

Neilson, Roger
c/o Maple Leaf Garden
60 Carlton St.
Toronto, Ontario
Canada M5B 1L1
hockey coach

Neiman Marcus Department Stores
Main and Ervay Sts.
Dallas, TX 75201
Richard Marcus, president

Nelson, Gaylord
Senate Office Building
Washington DC 20510
senator from Wisconsin

Nelson, Lindsey
45 E. 89th St.
New York, NY 10028
sportscaster

Nelson, Rick
c/o Willy Nelson
3300 W. Olive
Burbank, CA 91505
singer

Nelson, Willie
1201 16th Ave.
Nashville, TN 37212
singer, songwriter

Nero, Peter
c/o Leonard Franklin
666 5th Ave.
New York, NY 10019
pianist, conductor

Nessen, Ron
5112 Baltimore Ave.
Bethesda, MD 20016
former presidential
press secretary

Neto, Agostinho
Office of the President
Luanda, Angola
president of Angola

Neuman, Alfred E.
c/o *Mad*
485 Madison Ave.
New York, NY 10022
magazine mascot

Newhart, Bob
c/o Arthur Price
4024 Radford Ave.
Studio City, CA 91604
actor, comedian

Newley, Anthony
c/o Katz-Gallin-Morey
9255 Sunset Blvd. #1115
Los Angeles, CA 90069
singer, actor, songwriter

Newman, Barry
c/o APA
9000 Sunset Blvd. #315
Los Angeles, CA 90069
actor

Newman, Edwin
c/o NBC TV
30 Rockefeller Plaza
New York, NY 10020
journalist

Newman, Laraine
c/o NBC TV
30 Rockefeller Plaza
New York, NY 10020
comedienne

Newman, Paul
Colleytown Road
Westport, CT 06880
actor, race driver

Newman, Phyllis
c/o Richard Dickens
5550 Wilshire Blvd. #306
Los Angeles, CA 90036
singer, actress

Newman, Ralph
18 E. Chestnut St.
Chicago, IL 60611
Abraham Lincoln scholar

Newman, Randy
c/o Renaissance
Management Corp.
433 N. Camden Drive
Beverly Hills, CA 90210
singer, songwriter

Newman, Robert
919 Gravier St.
New Orleans, LA 70130
investor

Newmar, Julie
c/o Edgar Small
153 S. Robertson Blvd.
Beverly Hills, CA 90211
actress

Newton, Huey P.
8507 E. 14th St.
Oakland, CA 94620
founder/president of
Black Panther Party

Newton, Wayne
1504 S. Eastern Ave.
Las Vegas, NY 89107
entertainer

Newton-John, Olivia
9229 Sunset BLvd. #306
Los Angeles, CA 90069
singer, actress

New York Off-Track Betting Corporation
1501 Broadway
New York, NY 10036
Paul R. Screvane, chairman

Nichols, Mike
c/o Marvin B. Meyer
9601 Wilshire Blvd.
Beverly Hills, CA 90210
director, writer

Nicholson, Jack
c/o The Artists Agency
190 N. Canon Drive
Beverly Hills, CA 90210
actor

**Nichopoulos,
Dr. George**
1734 Madison
Memphis, TN 38104
personal physician to
late Elvis Presley

Nicklaus, Jack
321 Northlake Blvd.
Hwy. 1
North Palm Beach, FL 33408
golfer

Nigh, George
Office of the Governor
Oklahoma City, OK 73105
governor of Oklahoma

Nikolayeve-Tereshkova, Valent
Zvezdny Gorodik
Moscow, USSR
only woman ever to orbit earth

Nikolayev, Major Gen. Andrian
Zvezdny Gorodik
Moscow, USSR
orbited earth 64 times

Nilsson, Harry
c/o Bruce Grakal
9777 Wilshire Blvd. #1018
Los Angeles, CA 90212
singer, songwriter

Nimoy, Leonard
c/o Freeman & Doff
8732 Sunset Blvd. #250
Los Angeles, CA 90069
actor

Nisbet, Laura
2765 Prospect Ave.
La Crescentia, CA 91214
lived in iron lung longer than any living person (30 years)

Niven, David
c/o Jess Morgan
6300 Wilshire Blvd. #1100
Los Angeles, CA 90048
actor

Nixon, Patricia
142 E. 65th St.
New York, NY 10021
former first lady

Nixon, Richard
142 E. 65th St.
New York, NY 10021
former president

Nizer, Louis
40 W. 57th St.
New York, NY 10019
lawyer, author

Noguchi, Thomas
5670 Wilshire Blvd.
Los Angeles, CA 90036
Los Angeles County coroner

Noll, Chuck
c/o Pittsburgh Steelers
300 Stadium Circle
Pittsburgh, PA 15212
football coach

Nolte, Nick
c/o Mimi Webber
9200 Sunset Blvd. #810
Los Angeles, CA 90069
actor

Noojin, Dr. Ray
2661 10th Ave.
South Birmingham, AL 35205
dermatologist

Norris, Charles
P.O. Box 1236
Eustis, FL 32726
organizes tractor drag races

North, Alex
630 Resolano Drive
Pacific Palisades, CA 90272
composer

North, John Ringling
c/o Ringling Bros.-Barnum & Bailey Circus
Venice, FL 33578
nephew of Ringling Brothers circus family

Northwest Airlines
Mpls.-St. Paul
International Airport
St. Paul, MN 55111
Don Nyrop, president

Norton, Eleanor Homes
Equal Employment
Opportunity Commission
Washington, DC 20506
commission chairperson

Norton, Elliot
300 Harrison Ave.
Boston, MA 02106
drama critic

Norton, Ken
c/o Murray Goodman
232 Madison Ave.
New York, NY 10016
heavyweight boxer

Novack, Ben
c/o Fontainebleu Hotel
Miami Beach, FL 33140
hotel executive

Novack, Kim
c/o APA
9000 Sunset Blvd. #315
Los Angeles, CA 90069
actress

Nunn, Sam
Senate Office Building
Washington DC 20510
senator from Georgia

Nureyev, Rudolf
c/o S.A. Gorlinsky
35 Dover St.
London W1, England
ballet dancer

Nyad, Diana
Uptown Racquet Club
151 E. 86th St.
New York, NY 10022
long distance swimmer

Nyro, Laura
c/o Bernstein Productions
1260 Avenue of the Americas
New York, NY 10020
singer, songwriter

O'Brian, Hugh
c/o Contemporary-Korman
Artists
132 Lasky Drive
Beverly Hills, CA 90212
actor

O'Brien, Lawrence F.
c/o National Basketball Assn.
545 5th Ave.
New York, NY 10026
*basketball commissioner;
former National Democratic
Committee chairman whose
office was burglarized
at the Watergate*

O'Brien, Michael
1 Herald Plaza
Miami, FL 33132
photojournalist

O'Brien, Pat
466 N. Carmelina Drive
Los Angeles, CA 90049
actor

O'Connor, Carroll
P.O. Box 49514
Los Angeles, CA 90024
actor

O'Connor, Donald
c/o Loeb Management
233 S. Beverly Drive #121
Beverly Hills, CA 90212
actor, entertainer

**O'Hair, Madalyn
Murray**
4408 Medical Parkway
Austin, TX 78756
*atheist activist who
successfully waged campaign
to ban prayer in public schools*

O'Horgan, Tom
c/o Wm. Morris
151 El Camino Drive
Beverly Hills, CA 90212
composer

O'Jays
c/o Dan Cleary
9554 Wilshire Blvd.
Beverly Hills, CA 90210
music group

Ojemann, Dr. G.A.
University of Washington
Seattle, WA 98195
*neurosurgeon specializing
in seizure surgery*

Ojemann, Dr. R.G.
Massachusetts
General Hospital
32 Fruit St.
Boston, MA 02114
*neurosurgeon specializing in
cerebrovascular surgery
& acoustic tumors*

Old, John
Sloan-Kettering Institute
of Cancer Research
410 E. 68th St.
New York, NY 10021
cancer biologist

Oliver, Edith
c/o *New Yorker Magazine*
25 W. 43rd St.
New York, NY 10036
theatre critic

Oliver, James
New York Zoo Park
Bronx, NY 10460
zoologist

Oliver, Mary
Box 338
Provincetown, MA 02657
poet

**Olivier, Lord
Laurence**
Wheelshire Ltd.
33/34 Chancery Lane
London WC 2A IEN
England
actor

Olmsted, Mildred
1213 Rice St.
Philadelphia, PA, 19107
social worker

Olsen, Jack
7954 NE Baker Hill Road
Bainbridge Island, WA 98110
author

Olsen, Merlin
10271 W. Pico Blvd.
Los Angeles, CA 90064
*actor, sports
commentator*

Olsen, Dr. Norman
311 E. Chicago Ave.
Chicago, IL 60611
dentist

O'Malley, Walter
c/o L.A. Dodgers
1000 Elysian Park Ave.
Los Angeles, CA 90012
club president

Omand, Rev. Donald
Devon, England
exorcist

Onassis, Christina
Skorpios, Greece
business executive

Onassis, Jacqueline Kennedy
1040 5th Ave.
New York, NY 10028
widow of late John Kennedy and Aristotle Onassis

O'Neal, Ryan
c/o ICM
8899 Beverly Blvd.
Los Angeles, CA 90048
actor

O'Neal, Tatum
c/o ICM
8899 Beverly Blvd.
Los Angeles, CA 90048
actress

O'Neill, Jennifer
Long Meadow Road
Bedford Village, NY 10506
actress

O'Neill, Thomas P.
House Office Building
Washington DC 20515
speaker of the house

Ono, Yoko
c/o ATV Music
1330 Avenue of the Americas
New York, NY 10019
Mrs. John Lennon

Orbach, Jerry
232 W. 23rd St.
New York, NY 10011
actor

Orlando, Tony
c/o Wm. Morris
151 El Camino Drive
Beverly Hills, CA 90212
entertainer

Ormandy, Eugene
c/o Philadelphia
Orchestra Assn.
1420 Locust St.
Philadelphia, PA 19102
conductor

Orr, Bobby
c/o Chicago Black Hawks
1800 W. Madison St.
Chicago, IL 60612
hockey player

Osborn, Paul
1165 Park Ave.
New York, NY 10028
playwright

Osborne, Stellanova
Sault Ste Marie, MI 49783
author

Osmond, Donny
P.O. Box 5000
Provo, UT 84601
entertainer

Osmond, Marie
P.O. Box 5000
Provo, UT 84601
entertainer

Osrin, Raymond
1801 Superior Ave.
Cleveland, OH 44114
political cartoonist

Ostrow, Stuart
P.O. Box 188
Pound Ridge, NY 10576
theatrical producer

Oswald, Marina
c/o Mrs. Kenneth Porter
Heath, TX 75087
widow of Lee Harvey Oswald

Oswald, M.C.
4029 Byers
Ft. Worth, TX 76107
mother of Lee Harvey Oswald

Otis, James
10 S. Broadway #1340
St. Louis, MO 63102
football player

O'Toole, Peter
c/o Kohner-Levy Agency
9160 Sunset Blvd.
Los Angeles, CA 90069
actor

Overland, Mark
1602 Weatherwood Drive NW
Gig Harbor, WA 98335
researcher and photographer of killer whales

Owen, Jesse
333 N. Michigan Ave.
Chicago, IL 60601
public relations executive;
former Olympic champion

Ozawa, Selji
c/o Boston Symphony
Orchestra
Boston, MA 62101
conductor

Paar, Jack
c/o ABC TV
1330 Avenue of the Americas
New York, NY 10019
talk show host

Pacino, Al
c/o Wm. Morris
1350 Avenue of the Americas
New York, NY 10019
actor

Packwood, Robert
Senate Office Building
Washington DC 20510
senator from Oregon

Page, Alan
c/o Minnesotoa Vikings
110 France Ave.
Edina, MN 55435
attorney, retired football player

Page, Cornelius
Baruch College
P.O. Box 227
New York, NY 10010
linguist

Page, Edwin
Lynn Hall
Veterinary Medicine
Purdue University
West Lafayette, IN 47906
veterinarian

Page, Geraldine
c/o Stephen Draper
37 W. 57th St.
New York, NY 10019
actress

Page, Patti
c/o ICM
8899 Beverly Blvd.
Los Angeles, CA 90048
singer

Paige, Satchel
2626 E. 28th St.
Kansas City, MO 64128
member of baseball Hall of Fame

Paine Webber Stock Brokerage Co.
140 Broadway
New York, NY 10005
J.W. Davant, president

Pakula, Alan
c/o MGM Studios
10202 W. Washington Blvd.
Culver City, CA 90230
producer, director

Palance, Jack
c/o ICM
8899 Beverly Blvd.
Los Angeles, CA 90048
actor

Palestine Information Office
1326 18th St. NW
Washington DC 20036
Halem Hussaini, director

Palillo, Ron
c/o The Brokaw Company
9255 Sunset Blvd.
Los Angeles, CA 90069
actor

Palmer, Arnold
Arnold Palmer Aviation
R.D. Latrobe, PA 15650
golfer

Palmer Drug Abuse Program
3300 S. Gessner
Houston, TX 77080
Bob Meehan, consultant

Palmer, Jim
c/o Batimore Orioles
Memorial Stadium
Baltimore, MD 21218
baseball player

Palmer, Lilli
530 E. 86th St.
New York, NY 10028
actress

Palmer, Sandra
399 W. Camino Gardens Blvd.
Boca Raton, FL 33432
golfer

Pan Am World Airways
200 Park Ave.
New York, NY 10017
William T. Seawell, president

Pankey, Edgar
320 W. Main St.
Tustin, CA 92680
rancher

Papp, Joseph
c/o New York
Shakespeare Festival
425 Lafayette St.
New York, NY 10003
producer

Paramount Pictures Corp.
1 Gulf & Western Plaza
New York, NY 10023
Barry Diller, president

Pardee, Jack
P.O. Box 17247
Dulles
Washington DC 20041
football coach

Parents of Gays
201 W. 13th St.
New York, NY 10011
Jeanne Manford, chairperson

Parents Without Partners
7910 Woodmont Ave.
Suite 1000
Washington DC 20014
*Virginia L. Martin,
executive director*

Park, Tong Sun
South Korean Embassy
2320 Massachusetts Ave. NW
Washington DC 20008
*accused CIA
influence peddler*

Parker, Bruce
Department of Botany
Virgina Polytechnic Institute
Blacksburg, VA 24061
botanist

Parker, David
Swallow Hill Road
Pittsburgh, PA 15220
baseball player

Parker Pen Co.
Court & Division Sts.
Janesville, WI 53545
George Parker, president

Parkinson, Kenneth W.
1828 L St. NW
Washington DC 20036
civic leader

Parks, Bert
c/o Lenny-Debin Inc.
140 W. 58th St.
New York, NY 10019
entertainer

Parks, Dr. D.
Shriner's Burn Institute
University of Texas
Medical Branch Hospitals
Galveston, TX 77550
pediatric burn specialist

Parks, Rosa
c/o Rep. Conyers
305 Federal Building
231 W. Lafayette St.
Detroit, MI 48226
*credited with beginning civil
rights movement when she
refused to give up her seat and
move to the back of an
Alabama bus*

Parsons, Estelle
505 West End Ave.
New York, NY 10024
entertainer

Parsons, Roland Reading
Officers' Mess
RNZAF Base Ohakea
Private Bag, Palmerston Nort
New Zealand
*commanded first air balloo
to cross South Pole*

Partch, Virgil II
P.O. Box 725
Corona del Mar, CA 9262
*created concept of
newspaper comic strip*

Parton, Dolly
813 18th Ave. S.
Nashville, TN 37203
singer

Pastore, John. O.
Turkshead Building
Providence, RI 02903
former senator

Paterson, Basil A.
1625 Massachusetts Ave. NV
Washington DC 20036
politician

Patterson, Floyd
P.O. Box 336
New Paltz, NY 12561
*former world heavyweight
boxing champion*

Patterson, Francine
710 Middle Ave.
Menlo Park, CA 94025
*psychologist who has
established two-way
communication system
between humans and gorilla*

Patton, Gene
c/o Chuck Barris Productions
6430 Sunset Blvd.
Hollywood, CA 90028
"Gene, Gene, the Dancing Machine"

Paul, Arthur
919 N. Michigan Ave.
Chicago, IL 60611
designer of Playboy bunny logo

Paul, Les
78 Deerhaven Road
Mahwah, NJ 07430
inventor of 8-track recording

Paul, Mini
155 W. 68th St.
New York, NY 10023
ballet dancer

Paul, Wesley
9122 Farley
Overland Park, KS 66204
world's fastest 10-year-old marathon runner

Pauley, Jane
c/o NBC TV
30 Rockefeller Plaza
New York, NY 10020
talk show hostess, newscaster

Pauling, Dr. Linus C.
Linus Pauling Institute of Science and Medicine
2700 Sand Hill Road
Menlo Park, CA 94025
chemist

Paulsen, Pat
8170 Beverly Blvd. #104
Los Angeles, CA 90048
comedian

Pavarotti, Luciano
12 Lambroso
Modena, Italy 41100
singer

Payton, Walter
c/o Chicago Bears
55 E. Jackson St. Suite 1200
Chicago, IL 60604
football player

Peaches & Herb
c/o Polydor Records
6255 Sunset Blvd. Suite 1126
Los Angeles, CA 90028
singers

Peale, Norman Vincent
1025 5th Ave.
New York, NY 10028
clergyman, author

Pearl, Minnie
2708 Franklin Road
Nashville, TN 37204
entertainer

Pearson, Drew
c/o Dallas Cowboys
6116 N. Central Expressway
Dallas, TX 75206
football player

Pearson, Preston
c/o Dallas Cowboys
6116 N. Central Expressway
Dallas, TX 75206
football player

Peck, Gregory
P.O. Box 49294
Los Angeles, CA 90049
actor

Pei, I.M.
600 Madison Ave.
New York, NY 10022
architect

Pele
c/o Warner Communications
75 Rockefeller Plaza
New York, NY 10019
former soccer star

Pell, Claiborne
Senate Office Building
Washington DC 20510
senator from Rhode Island

Pendergrass, Teddy
c/o Alive Enterprises
8600 Melrose Ave.
Los Angeles, CA 90069
singer

Penn Central Transportation
6 Penn Center Plaza
Philadelphia, PA 19104
Jervis Langdon Jr., president

Penn, Irving
P.O. Box 934
FDR Station
New York, NY 10022
photographer

J.C. Penney Company
1301 Avenue of the Americas
New York, NY 10019
Donald Seibert, president

Peppard, George
c/o Stan Rosenfield
9229 Sunset Blvd.
Los Angeles, CA 90069
actor

Pepper, Claude
House Office Building
Washington DC 20515
U.S. representative

**Pepsi-Cola
Company Inc.**
Anderson Hill Road
Purchase, NY 10577
Donald Kendall, president

Percy, Charles H.
Senate Office Building
Washington DC 20510
senator from Illinois

Perkins, Anthony
c/o ICM
8899 Beverly Blvd.
Los Angeles, CA 90048
actor

Perot, H. Ross
c/o Electronic Data Systems
7171 Forest Lane
Dallas, TX 75230
philanthropist

Perrine, Valerie
c/o Bernie Francis
328 S. Beverly Drive
Beverly Hills, CA 90212
actress

Perry, Frank
655 Park Ave.
New York, NY 10021
director

Perry, Gaylord
P.O. Box 509
Williamston, NC 27892
baseball player

Pescow, Donna
c/o Kohner-Levy Agency
9169 Sunset Blvd.
Los Angeles, CA 90069
actress

Peters, Bernadette
c/o ICPR
9255 Sunset Blvd.
Los Angeles, CA 90069
actress, singer

Peters, Jon
c/o First Artists
4000 Warner Blvd.
Burbank, CA 91522
producer

Peters, Roberta
c/o ICM
40 W. 57th St.
New York, NY 10019
opera singer

Peters, Svetlana
50 Wilson Road
Princeton, NJ 08540
*author, daughter of
Joseph Stalin*

Petersen, Robert E.
8490 Sunset Blvd.
Los Angeles, CA 90069
publisher

Peterson, Elly
1525 M St. NW #602
Washington DC 20005
*co-chairperson, ERAmerica
(organization fighting for
Equal Rights Amendment)*

Peterson, Henry E.
916 Dalevien Drive
Silver Springs, MD 20901
*former justice department
official*

Peterson, James
8530 Wilshire Blvd.
Beverly Hills, CA 90211
marriage counselor

Peterson, Oscar
c/o Regal Records Ltd.
124 8th St.
Toronto, Ontario
Canada M8V 3CV
pianist

Peterson, Peter
c/o Lehman Brothers
2 S. Williams St.
New York, NY 10004
former secretary of commerce

Peterson, Russell
Council on Environmental
Quality
722 Jackson Place
Washington DC 20006
environmentalist

Peterson, Val
710 E. 7th St.
P.O. Box 351
Wayne, NE 68787
former ambassador

Petty, Richard
Route #3
P.O. Box 621
Randleman, NC 27317
auto racer

Philaret
5 E. 93rd St.
New York, NY 10028
*primate, Russian
Orthodox Church*

Phillips, Dorothy
Corcoran Gallery of Art
7th & E St. NW
Washington DC 20006
art curator

Phillips, Mackenzie
c/o CBS TV
800 Beverly Blvd.
Los Angeles, CA 90036
actress

Phillips, Michelle
c/o A&M Records
1416 N. La Brea Ave.
Los Angeles, CA 90028
actress, singer

**Phillips, Petroleum
Company**
Phillips Building
Bartlesville, OK 74004
W.F. Martin, president

Pidgeon, Walter
30 Strada Corte Road
Los Angeles, CA 90024
actor

Pierson, Frank
c/o Ziegler Associates
9255 Sunset Blvd.
Los Angeles, CA 90069
writer, director

Piggy, Miss
115 E. 57th St.
New York, NY 10022
muppet

Pike, Otis G.
House Office Building
Washington, DC 20515
U.S. representative

Pilch, Dr. Y.
Harbor General Hospital
1000 Carson St.
Torrance, CA 90502
*surgeon specializing in
breast cancer*

Pillsbury Company
608 2nd Ave.
Minneapolis, MN 55402
William Spoor, president

Pinkham, Mary Ellen
c/o Warner Books
75 Rockefeller Plaza
New York, NY 10019
helpful hints author

Pinter, Harold
c/o David Fromkin
950 3rd Ave.
New York, NY 10022
playwright

Piper, Geraldine
9200 Sunset Blvd. Suite 1210
Los Angeles, CA 90069
nutritionist

**Planned Parenthood
of America**
810 7th Ave.
New York, NY 10019
*Henrietta Marshall,
chairperson*

Plant, Robert
c/o Swan Song
444 Madison Ave,
New York, NY 10022
lead singer, Led Zeppelin

Player, Gary
c/o International
Management Inc.
767 5th Ave.
New York, NY 10022
golfer

Pleshette, Suzanne
c/o ICM
8899 Beverly Blvd.
Los Angeles, CA 90048
actress

Plimpton, George
541 E. 72nd St.
New York, NY 10021
author

Plummer, Christopher
c/o Wm. Morris
1350 Avenue of the Americas
New York, NY 10019
actor

Plunkett, Jim
c/o San Francisco '49ers
Candlestick Park
San Francisco, CA 94124
football player

Podhoretz, Norman
165 E. 56th St.
New York, NY 10022
editor

Pointer Sisters
c/o Adam's Dad Mgmt.
827 Folsom St.
San Francisco, CA 94107
music group

Poitier, Sidney
c/o Verdon Productions
9350 Wilshire Blvd.
Beverly Hills, CA 90212
actor

Polar Bear Club
Chamber of Commerce Bldg.
Coney Island, NY 11224
*Alexander R. Mottola,
president (winter swimmers'
club)*

Polaroid Corporation
549 Technology Square
Cambridge, MA 02139
Edwin H. Land, chairman

Poll, Martin
919 3rd Ave.
New York, NY 10022
producer

Pollack, Sydney
c/o Warner Brothers
4000 Warner Blvd.
Burbank, CA 91522
director

Pool, John
166 East Ave.
Norwalk, Ct 06851
cancer surgeon

Porter, Sylvia
30 E. 42nd St.
New York, NY 10017
financial writer

Porter, William J.
U.S. State Department
Washington DC 20520
ambassador to Saudi Arabia

Porthault, D.
57 E. 57th St.
New York, NY 10022
linen designer

Portillo, Jose Lopez
Office of the President
Mexico City, Mexico
president of Mexico

Powell, Jane
1364 Stradella Road
Los Angeles, CA 90024
actress, singer

Powell, Jody
The White House
Washington DC 20500
presidential press secretary

Powell, Lewis
U.S. Supreme Court
Washington DC 20543
justice

Powell, W.E.
800 Downtowner Blvd.
Mobile, AK 36609
*organizer of oyster-shucking
crab-picking and seafood-
tasting contests*

Powell, William
Palm Springs, CA 92262
actor

Powers, Stephanie
c/o Wm. Morris
1350 Avenue of the America
New York, NY 10019
actress

Preminger, Otto
711 5th Ave.
New York, NY 10022
producer, director

Prentiss, Paula
c/o Phil Gersh Agency
222 N. Canon Drive
Beverly Hills, CA 90210
actress

Presley, Priscilla
c/o Wm. Morris
151 El Camino Drive
Beverly Hills, CA 90212
*former wife of late
Elvis Presley*

Press, Frank
Executive Office Building
Washington DC 20500
*director, Office of Science &
Technology Policy*

Pressler, Larry
Senate Office Building
Washington DC 20510
senator from South Dakota

Preston, Billy
c/o A&M Records
1416 N. La Brea Ave.
Los Angeles, CA 90028
singer, musician

Preston, Robert
c/o Springer & Associates
667 Madison Ave.
New York, NY 10021
actor, singer

Preus, Jacob A.
Missouri Synod
500 N. Broadway
St. Louis, MO 63102
president, Lutheran Church

Previn, Andre
c/o Harrison/Parrott Ltd.
22 Hillgate St.
London W8, England
composer, conductor

Previn, Dory
c/o Ivan Hoffman
2040 Avenue of the Stars
Los Angeles, CA 90067
singer, songwriter

Price, Roger
c/o Price/Stern/Sloan
Publishers
410 North La Cienega Blvd.
Los Angeles, CA 90048
writer, comedian, actor

Price/Stern/Sloan Publishers, Inc.
410 N. La Cienega Blvd.
Los Angeles, CA 90048
L.L. Sloan, president

Price, Vincent
c/o ICM
8899 Beverly Blvd.
Los Angeles, CA 90048
actor

Pride, Charley
c/o Chardon Inc.
P.O. Box 40167
Nashville, TN 37204
singer

Prince, Harold
1270 Avenue of the Americas
New York, NY 10020
theatrical producer

Principal, Victoria
c/o CBS TV
7800 Beverly Blvd.
Los Angeles, CA 90036
actress

Pritikin, Dr. Nathan
c/o Grosset & Dunlap
51 Madison Ave.
New York, NY 10010
diet specialist; author

Pritikin, Roland
Talcott Building
Rockford, IL 61101
eye surgeon

Proctor & Gamble
310 E. 6th St.
Cincinnati, OH 45202
Edward Harness, president

Prowse, Juliet
c/o John Mucci & Associates
9200 Sunset Blvd. #905
Los Angeles, CA 90069
dancer, entertainer

Proxmire, William
Senate Office Building
Washington DC 20510
senator from Wisconsin

Prudential Insurance Company
Prudential Plaza
Newark, NJ 07101
Donald MacNaughton, president

Pruitt, Dr. B.
Brooke Army Medical Center
San Antonio, TX 78235
adult and pediatric burn specialist

Pruitt, Greg
c/o Cleveland Browns
Cleveland Stadium
Cleveland, OH 44114
football player

Pryor, David H.
Senate Office Building
Washington DC 20510
senator from Arkansas

Pryor, Richard
8560 Sunset Blvd. #706
Los Angeles, CA 90069
comedian, actor

Pursch, Capt. Joseph
Long Beach Naval Regional
Medical Center
Long Beach, CA 90801
director of alcohol rehabilitation program; patients include Betty Ford and Billy Carter

Puzo, Mario
c/o Putnam's
200 Madison Ave.
New York, NY 10016
author

Quaker Oats Company
Merchandise Mart Plaza
Chicago, IL 60654
Robert Stuart, president

Queen
c/o John Reid Entertainments
211 S. Beverly Drive #200
Beverly Hills, CA 90212
music group

Quie, Al
Office of the Governor
St. Paul, MN 55155
governor of Minnesota

Quilligan, Dr. E.J.
University of Southern Calif.
2025 Zonal Ave.
Los Angeles, CA 90033
high-risk pregnancy expert

Quinn, Anthony
c/o ICPR
9255 Sunset Blvd.
Los Angeles, CA 90069
actor

Quinn, Carmel
Park Ave.
Leonia, NJ 07024
singer

Quinn, Sally
c/o *Washington Post*
1150 15th St. NW
Washington DC 20005
journalist

Quinn, Tom
California Air Resources
Board
Sacramento, CA 95812
board director

R2D2 (Artoo-Detoo)
Lucasfilms
P.O. Box 8669
Universal City, CA 91608
robot

RCA Corporation
30 Rockefeller Plaza
New York, NY 10020
Edgar Griffiths, president

RKO General
1440 Broadway
New York, NY 10018
Frank J. Shakespeare, president

Rabe, David
c/o Ellen Heuwald
905 West End Ave.
New York, NY 10025
playwright

Rabin, Yitzhak
Jerusalem, Israel
former premier of Israel

Radio Free Europe
1201 Connecticut Ave. NW
Washington DC 20036
Glenn Ferguson, director

Radner, Gilda
c/o NBC TV
30 Rockefeller Plaza
New York, NY 10020
comedienne

Radziwill, Lee Bouvier
c/o John Carl Warnecke & Associates
745 5th Ave.
New York, NY 10022
interior designer

Rafshoon, Gerald
The White House
Washington DC 20500
public relations assistant to President Carter

Raft, George
2200 Avenue of the Stars
Los Angeles, CA 90067
actor

Rahman, General Ziaur
Office of the President
Daca, Bangladesh
president of Bangladesh

Railsback, Thomas F.
House Office Building
Washington DC 20515
U.S. representative

Rainier III, Prince (Grimaldi)
The Palace
Principality of Monaco
ruler of Monaco

Raitt, Bonnie
c/o Avalon Productions
8 Locke St.
Cambridge, MA 02140
singer

Ralston Purina Company
835 S. 8th St.
St. Louis, MO 63102
Hal R. Dean, president

Ramada Inn
3838 E. Van Buren St.
Phoenix, AZ 85008
Marion Isbell, president

Ramirez, Raul
Avenida Ruiz
65 Sur Ensenada
Baja California, Mexico
tennis player

Ramsey, William
c/o Seestrasse
630 8706
Mellen, Switzerland
singer

Rand McNally Map Company
8255 N. Central Park Ave.
Skokie, IL 60076
Andrew McNally, president

Rand, Dr. R.
UCLA
10883 Le Conte Blvd.
Los Angeles, CA 90024
neurosurgeon specializing in microsurgery

Randall, Robert
c/o Alice O'Leary
2317 M St. NW
Washington DC 20037
only person legally allowed to smoke marijuana in the U.S. (to relieve glaucoma)

Randall, Tony
c/o Diamond Artists
8400 Sunset Blvd.
Los Angeles, CA 90069
actor

Randolph, Dr. J.
Children's Hospital-National
Medical Center
2125 13th St. NW
Washington DC 20009
pediatric burn specialist

Randolph, Jennings
Senate Office Building
Washington DC 20510
senator from West Virginia

**Randolph, Thomas
Jefferson**
P.O. Box 881
Charlottesville, VA 22901
*great-great-great-great-
grandson of Thomas Jefferson*

Rangel, Charles B.
House Office Building
Washington DC 20515
U.S. representative

Ransohoff, Dr. J.
N.Y. University
Medical School
550 1st Ave.
New York, NY 10016
*neurosurgeon specializing
in cerebrovascular
tumor surgery*

Rather, Dan
c/o CBS News
524 W. 57th St.
New York, NY 10019
journalist

Rawls, Lou
c/o Walter Scott
6430 Sunset Blvd.
Hollywood, CA 90028
singer

Ray, Dixy Lee
Office of the Governor
State Capitol
Olympia, WA 98504
governor of Washington

Ray, Ed
Chowchilla, CA 93610
*school bus driver who saved
hijacked bus and children*

Ray, Elizabeth
c/o Mark Korman
Management
200 W. 57th St.
New York, NY 10019
*former mistress
of Wayne Hays*

Ray, James Earl
Brushy Mountain Prison
Petro, TN 37845
*convicted assassin of
Martin Luther King Jr.*

Ray, Robert D.
Office of the Governor
Des Moines, IA 50319
governor of Iowa

Rayburn, Gene
Sea View Ave.
Osterville, MA 02655
game show host

Raye, Martha
c/o Fitzgerald Company
9000 Sunset Blvd.
Los Angeles, CA 90069
entertainer

Raymond, Gene
9570 Wilshire Blvd.
Beverly Hills, CA 90212
actor, producer

Re, Edward D.
One Federal Plaza
New York, NY 10007
*chief judge, U.S.
Customs Court*

Read, Curtis
1820 N. La Brea Ave., Apt. 2
Hollywood, CA 90028
*human mannequin who can
stand motionless for 3½ hours*

Reagan, Ronald
10960 Wilshire Blvd.
Los Angeles, CA 90024
*former governor, actor;
presidential candidate*

Reasoner, Harry
c/o CBS News
524 W. 57th St.
New York, NY 10019
journalist

Rebozo, Charles G. "Bebe"
95 W. McIntire St.
Key Biscayne, FL 33149
businessman, friend of Richard Nixon

Reddy, Helen
c/o Jeff Wald Associates
9356 Santa Monica Blvd.
Beverly Hills, CA 90210
singer

Redenbacher, Orville
c/o Hunt-Wesson Foods
1645 W. Valencia Drive
Fullerton, CA 92634
popcorn king

Redford, Robert
c/o Pickwick
545 Madison Ave.
New York, NY 10022
actor

Redgrave, Lynn
205 W. 57th St.
New York, NY 10019
actress

Redgrave, Vanessa
c/o Pickwick
9744 Wilshire Blvd.
Beverly Hills, CA 90212
actress

Reed, Donna
300 S. Colgems Square
Burbank, CA 91506
actress

Reed, Jerry
1107 18th Ave. S.
Nashville, TN 37212
singer, musician

Reed, Rex
220 E. 42nd St.
New York, NY 10017
entertainment critic

Reed, Willis
4 Penn Plaza
New York, NY 10001
basketball player

Reese, Mason
325 West End Ave.
New York, NY 10023
actor

Reeve, Christopher
c/o Stak Hesseltine
119 W. 57th St.
New York, NY 10019
actor

Rehnquist, William H.
U.S. Supreme Court
Washington DC 20543
justice

Reichelderfer, Francis
U.S. National
Weather Service
Gramar Building
Silver Springs, MD 20852
meteorologist

Reiner, Carl
c/o CBS
4024 Radford Ave.
Studio City, CA 91604
actor, writer, director

Reiner, Rob
c/o Creative Artists Agency
1888 Century Park E.
Suite 1400
Los Angeles, CA 90067
actor, writer

Reinholdt, Mrs. I.
900 Preston Ave. #1
Houston, TX 77002
owner of mail order company specializing in x-rated merchandise

Remick, Lee
c/o ICM
8899 Beverly Blvd.
Los Angeles, CA 90048
actress

Resorts International
Boardwalk & North
Carolina Ave.
Atlantic City, NJ 08484
Anthony Rey, president

Revlon Inc.
767 5th Ave.
New York, NY 10022
Michael C. Bergerac, president

Reynold, Paul
12 E. 41st St.
New York, NY 10017
literary agent

Reynolds, Burt
c/o ICM
8899 Beverly Blvd.
Los Angeles, CA 90048
actor

Reynolds, Debbie
c/o Creative Artists Agency
1888 Century Park E.
Suite 1400
Los Angeles, CA 90067
entertainer, actress

Reynolds, Ed
P.O. Box 923
Vineland, NJ 08360
leader, American Nazi Party

Reynolds, Frank
c/o ABC News
1330 Avenue of the Americas
New York, NY 10019
journalist

**Reynolds, Harry
& Jean**
Benson, AZ 85602
*married couple who both
underwent sex
change operations*

**R.J. Reynolds
Tobacco Company**
Winston-Salem, NC 27102
William Hobbs, president

Rhodes, James A.
Office of the Governor
State House
Columbus, OH 43215
governor of Ohio

Rhodes, John J.
House Office Building
Washington DC 20515
U.S. representative

Ribicoff, Abraham A.
Senate Office Building
Washington DC 20510
senator from Connecticut

Rice, Jim
c/o Red Sox
24 Yawkey Way
Boston, MA 12215
baseball player

Rice-Wray, Edris
Universidad de las Americas
Apt. Postal 13
St. al Catarina Martin
Puebla, Mexico
author, family planner

Rich, Adam
c/o ABC TV
4151 Prospect Ave.
Los Angeles, CA 90027
actor

Rich, Alan
755 20th Ave.
New York, NY 10017
music critic

Rich, Buddy
c/o Wm. Morris
1350 Avenue of the Americas
New York, NY 10019
drummer

Rich, Charlie
8229 Rockcreek Parkway
Cordova, TN 38018
singer

Richards, Renee
c/o Frank Froehling
P.O. Box 1932
Stuart, FL 23404
tennis player, transsexual

Richardson, Elliot
U.S. State Department
Washington DC 20520
*ambassador, Law of
the Sea Conference*

Richardson, Howard
207 Columbus Ave.
New York, NY 10023
playwright

Rickles, Don
8966 Sunset Blvd.
Los Angeles, CA 90069
entertainer

Rickover, Hyman G.
U.S. Energy Research &
Development Administration
Washington DC 20010
government official

Riddle, Nelson
c/o William Alexander
660 Madison Ave.
New York, NY 10021
composer, conductor

Rideout, Greta
c/o Christensen
695 Ferry SE
Salem, OR 97301
*first woman to prosecute
her husband for rape*

Riegle, Donald W. Jr.
Senate Office Building
Washington DC 20510
senator from Michigan

Rifkind, Simon H.
345 Park Ave.
New York, NY 10022
attorney

Rigby, Kathy
P.O. Box 6046
San Bernardino, CA 92410
gymnast, sports commentator

Rigg, Diana
c/o Redway & Associates
5-11 Mortimer St.
London, England
WIN 7RH
actress

Riggs, Bobby
508 E Ave.
Coronado, CA 92118
tennis player

Riley, Richard W.
Office of the Governor
Columbia, NC 29211
governor of North Carolina

Ringer, Robert J.
c/o Funk & Wagnall
666 5th Ave.
New York, NY 10019
author

Ringling Bros. & Barnum & Bailey Circus
1015 18th St. NW #1100
Washington DC 20036
Irvin Feld, president

Rippy, Rodney Allan
c/o Dorothy Day Otis
6430 Sunset Blvd.
Los Angeles, VA 90028
actor

Ritter, John
c/o L. Frank Company
1801 Avenue of the Stars
Los Angeles, CA 90067
actor

Rivera, Geraldo
c/o ABC News
1330 Avenue of the Americas
New York, NY 10023
journalist

Rivers, Joan
P.O. Box 777
Los Angeles, CA 90049
comedienne

Rivlin, Dr. Alice M.
Congressional Budget Office
U.S. Congress
Washington DC 20515
economist

Rizzo, Frank
City Hall Room 215
Philadelphia, PA 19107
former mayor of Philadelphia

Rizzuto, Phil
c/o WMCA
888 7th Ave,
New York, NY 10019
baseball announcer

Robards, Jason
Shore Haven Road
Norwalk, CT 06855
actor

Robb, Charles
Office of the Lt. Governor
State Capitol
Richmond, VA 23219
lt. governor of Virginia

Robb, Lynda Johnson
641 Lexington Ave.
New York, NY 10022
daughter of late president Lyndon Johnson

Robbins, Harold
c/o Simon & Schuster
1230 6th Ave.
New York, NY 10009
author

Robbins, Jerome
c/o New York City Ballet
New York State Theatre
Lincoln Center
New York, NY 10023
choreographer

Robbins, Marty
713 18th Ave.
S. Nashville, TN 37203
musician

Roberts, Eric
c/o Bill Treusch
853 7th Ave. Suite 9A
New York, NY 10019
actor

Roberts, Oral
Abundant Life Building
Tulsa, OK 74112
evangelist

Roberts, Pernell
c/o Ted Witzer
1900 Avenue of the Stars
Suite 2850
Los Angeles, CA 90067
actor

Roberts, Tony
c/o Wm. Morris
1350 Avenue of the Americas
New York, NY 10019
actor

Robertson, Cliff
c/o ICM
8899 Beverly Blvd.
Los Angeles, CA 90048
actor

Robertson, James D.
132 Oak Drive
Durham, NC 27707
anatomist

Robinson, Earl
3929 Calle Cita
Santa Barbara, CA 93110
composer

Robinson, Frank
Aqua Verde Drive
Bel Air, CA 90024
*first black manager of a
professional baseball team*

Robinson, Smokey
c/o Don Foster
6255 Sunset Blvd.
Los Angeles, CA 90028
singer, songwriter

Rockefeller, David
1 Chase Manhattan Bank
New York, NY 10015
banker

Rockefeller, Happy
Pocantico Hills
North Tarrytown, NY 10591
*widow of late
Nelson Rockefeller*

**Rockefeller,
John D. III**
30 Rockefeller Plaza
New York, NY 10020
businessman

**Rockefeller,
John D. IV**
Office of the Governor
State Capitol
Charleston, WV 25305
governor of West Virginia

**Rockefeller,
Lawrence**
Rockefeller Bros. Fund
30 Rockefeller Plaza
Room 5600
New York, NY 10020
fund chairman

Rockettes, The
Radio City Music Hall
1260 Avenue of the America
New York, NY 10020
chorus line

**Rockwell
International**
600 Grant St.
Pittsburgh, PA 15219
W. F. Rockwell Jr., presiden

Roddenberry, Gene
c/o Paramount TV
5451 Marathon St.
Hollywood, CA 90038
*creator and producer
of "Star Trek"*

Rodino, Peter
House Office Building
Washington, DC 20515
*house impeachment
committee chairman*

Rogers, Edmund
7733 Forsyth
St. Louis, MO 63105
patent lawyer

Rogers, Ginger
Rogers Rogue River Ranch
Rt. 14-R, Box 432
Eagle Point, OR 97524
dancer, actress

Rogers, Kenny
c/o Kragen Company
1112 N. Sherbourne Drive
Los Angeles, CA 90069
singer, songwriter, actor

Rogers, Roy
c/o Art Rush
10221 Riverside Drive
N. Hollywood, CA 91602
singer, actor

Rogers, William
1229 19th St. NW
Washington DC 20036
former secretary of state

Rohatyn, Felix G.
1 Rockefeller Foundation
111 W. 50th St.
New York, NY 10022
*foundation chairman;
directed New York City's
financial reconstruction*

Roland, Gilbert
518 N. Roxbury Drive
Beverly Hills, CA 90210
actor

Rolle, Esther
c/o Rosenfield Associates
9229 Sunset Blvd.
Los Angeles, CA 90069
actress

Rolling Stones
c/o Sir Productions
130 W. 57th St.
New York, NY 10019
music group

Rollins, Betty
c/o The New
American Library
1301 Avenue of the Americas
New York, NY 10019
journalist

Rollins, Sonny
Route 9G
Germantown, NY 12526
musician

**Rolls-Royce
Owner's Club**
Green Oak Farm
Kingsville, MD 21087
John C. Love, secretary

Romero, Cesar
12115 San Vicente Blvd.
Los Angeles, CA 90049
actor

Romney, George
12 E. 87th St.
New York, NY 10028
*former governor of Michigan;
former HUD secretary*

Ronan, William J.
New York University
New York, NY 10016
*professor; port
authority chairman*

Ronstadt, Linda
644 Doheny Drive
Los Angeles, CA 90069
singer

Rooney, Andy
c/o CBS
524 W. 57th St.
New York, NY 10019
humorist

Rooney, Art Sr.
c/o Pittsburgh Steelers
300 Stadium Circle
Pittsburgh, PA 15212
team founder and owner

Rooney, John J.
217 Congress St.
Brooklyn, NY 11201
former congressman

Rooney, Mickey
c/o Tobias & Associates
1901 Avenue of the Stars
Suite 840
Los Angeles, CA 90067
actor

**Roosevelt,
Theodore III**
5 Penn Center Plaza
Philadelphia, PA 19103
investment executive

Rose, David
4020 Longridge Ave.
Sherman Oaks, CA 91403
composer

Rose Marie
233 S. Beverly Drive
Suite 121
Beverly Hills, CA 90210
entertainer

Rose, Pete
c/o Philadelphia Phillies
Veterans' Stadium
Broad St.
Philadelphia, PA 19148
baseball player

Rosenburg, Dr. S.A.
Stanford University
Medical Center
Stanford, CA 94305
chemotherapy specialist

**Rosenkowlitz,
Colin & Sarah**
Cape Town, South Africa
*parents of world's only
surviving sextuplets*

Ross, Diana
c/o Motown Records
6255 Sunset Blvd.
Hollywood, CA 90028
singer, actress

Ross, Katherine
c/o Hiller Agency
9220 Sunset Blvd.
Los Angeles, CA 90069
actress

Ross, Margaret
1830 Trapelo Road
Waltham, MA 02154
nutritionist

Roth, Phillip
c/o Farrar, Strauss & Giroux
15 Union Square W.
New York, NY 10022
author

Roth, William V. Jr.
Senate Office Building
Washington DC 20510
senator from Delaware

Rothschild, Louis
1629 K St. NW
Washington DC 20006
businessman

Roundtree, Richard
c/o APA
9000 Sunset Blvd. Suite 315
Los Angeles, CA 90069
actor

Rowlands, Gena
c/o Chandlee
9056 Santa Monica Blvd.
Los Angeles, CA 90069
actress

Rozelle, Pete
c/o National Football League
410 Park Ave.
New York, NY 10016
league commissioner

Rubicam, Raymond
87 Mouttan Shadows
Scottsdale, AZ 85253
*founder, Young-Rubicam
Advertising Agency*

Rubin, Jerry C.
c/o M. Evans & Co. Inc.
216 E. 49th St.
New York, NY 10017
political activist

Rubinstein, Artur
22 Square de l'Avenue Foch
Paris 16 Leme, France
pianist

Helena Rubinstein Inc.
300 Park Ave.
New York, NY 10022
Oscar Kolin, chairman

Ruckelshaus, William
c/o Weyerhauser Company
2525 S. 36th St.
Federal Way
Tacoma, WA 98401
*attorney, former acting FBI
director*

Ruddy, Al
c/o Paramount Studio
5451 Marathon St.
Los Angeles, CA 90038
producer

Ruether, Rosemary
2131 Brummel St.
Evanston, IL 60202
theologian

Rumsfeld, Donald H.
c/o G.D. Searle & Company
Skokie, IL 60076
former secretary of defense

Rush, Kenneth
3147 O St. NW
Washington DC 20007
former ambassador

Rusk, Dean
1 Lafayette Square
620 Hill St.
Athens, GA 30601
former secretary of state

Russell, Jane
13527 Leadwell St.
Van Nuys, CA 91405
actress

Russell, Ken
c/o Warner Brothers
75 Rockefeller Plaza
New York, NY 10019
director

Russell, Kurt
c/o McHugh Agency
8150 Beverly Blvd. Suite 206
Los Angeles, CA 90048
actor

Russell, Leon
c/o Shelter Records
5112 Hollywood Blvd.
Hollywood, CA 90028
singer, songwriter

Russell, Nipsy
c/o Joseph Rapp
1650 Broadway
New York, NY 10019
comedian

**Russell Stover
Candies**
1004 Baltimore St.
Kansas City, MO 64105
Louis Ward, president

Russo, Anthony J. Jr.
168 Broadway
New York, NY 10038
*helped disclose
Pentagon Papers*

Rustin, Bayard
260 Park Ave. S.
New York, NY 10010
civil rights activist

Ruth, Mrs. Babe
c/o New York Yankees
Yankee Stadium
Bronx, NY 10451
widow of Babe Ruth

Ryan, Mrs. Leo
300 Davey Glenn Road
Belmont, CA 94002
widow of slain congressman

Ryan, Nolan
P.O. Box 288
Houston, TX 77001

baseball player

Saad, Dr. Samia Galal
High Institute of Public Health
Environmental Health Dept.
165 El-Horreya Ave.
Alexandria, Egypt
civil engineer developing systems to prevent water pollution in developing nations

Sackler, Howard
45 E. 10th St.
New York, NY 10011
playwright

Sadat, Anwar
Office of the President
Cairo, Egypt
president of Egypt

Safer, Morley
c/o CBS News
524 W. 57th St.
New York, NY 10019
journalist

Safeway Stores
45th & Jackson Sts.
Oakland, CA 94660
W.S. Mitchell, president

Sagan, Carl
c/o Doubleday & Company
245 Park Ave.
New York, NY 10017
astronomer, author

Sager, Carol Bayer
c/o Elektra Records
962 N. La Cienega Blvd.
Los Angeles, CA 90069
singer, songwriter

Sahl, Mort
c/o Durgom
9229 Sunset Blvd. #615
Los Angeles, CA 90069
satirist

Saidy, Anthony
2 Cedar Lane
Douglaston, NY 11363
chess master

Saint, Eva Marie
c/o Creative Artists Agency
1888 Century Park E.
Suite 1400
Los Angeles, CA 90067
actress

St. Clair, James
28 State St.
Boston, MA 02109
Nixon's Watergate counsel

St. James, Susan
9134 Sunset Blvd. Suite 909
Los Angeles, CA 90069
actress

St. John, Jill
c/o Chasin-Park-Citron
10889 Wilshire Blvd.
Los Angeles, CA 90024
actress

Saint-Subber, Arnold
116 E. 64th St.
New York, NY 10021
theatrical producer

Sakharov, Andrei D.
Gorki, USSR
soviet dissident

Salant, Richard
c/o CBS News
524 W. 57th St.
New York, NY 10019
president, CBS News

Sales, Soupy
Soupbone Corp.
5800 Sunset Blvd.
Hollywood, CA 90028
comedian

Salinger, J.D.
c/o Harold Ober & Associates
40 W. 49th St.
New York, NY 10017
author

Salinger, Pierre E.
9101 Hazen Drive
Beverly Hills ,CA 90211
former presidential press secretary

Salk, Jonas
P.O. Box 1809
San Diego, CA 92112
developer of polio vaccine

Saltzman, Harry
c/o Mike Beck
729 7th Ave.
New York, NY 10019
producer

Salvation Army
120 W. 14th St.
New York, NY 10011
Paul S. Kaiser, commander

Salvino, Carmen
2658 N. New England
Chicago, IL 60635
bowler

Sampson, Linden Forbes
Office of the Prime Minister
Georgetown, Guyana
prime minister of Guyana

Samuels, Howard S.
355 Lexington Ave.
New York, NY 10017
founder of New York City's off-track betting corporation

Samuels, Ron
280 S. Beverly Drive #309
Beverly Hills, CA 90212
talent manager

Sanders, Col. Harland
KFC Corporation
P.O. Box 13331
Louisville, KY 40213
founder, Kentucky Fried Chicken Restaurants

Sanford, Isabel
c/o Mary Ellen White
151 N. San Vincente Blvd.
Beverly Hills, CA 90211
actress

Santini, Brothers Moving Co.
1405 Jerome Ave.
Bronx, NY 10452
Godfrey Santini, president

Sara Lee Kitchens
500 Waukegan Road
Deerfield, IL 60015
William P. Mahoney, president

Sarbanes, Paul S.
Senate Office Building
Washington, DC 20510
senator from Maryland

Sardi's Restaurant
234 W. 44th St.
New York, NY 10036
Vincent Sardi, owner

Sarnoff, Dorothy
Speech Dynamics Inc.
111 W. 57th St.
New York, NY 10019
voice trainer

Sarnoff, Robert W.
30 Rockefeller Plaza
New York, NY 10020
corporate businessman

Sartre, Jean-Paul
42 rue Bonapart
Paris 6e
France
philosopher, author, playwright

Sasser, James R.
Senate Office Building
Washington DC 20510
senator from Tennessee

Sassoon, Vidal
1801 Century Park E.
Los Angeles, CA 90067
hair stylist

Savalas, Telly
c/o ICM
8899 Beverly Blvd.
Los Angeles, CA 90048
actor

Save the Children Federation
48 Wilton Road
Westport, CT 06880
David L. Guyer, president

Saxbe, William B.
Route 2
Mechanicsburg, OH 43044
former ambassador

Saxon, John
1851 Kimberly Lane
Los Angeles, CA 90049
actor

Sayers, Gale
Southern Illinois University
Carbondale, IL 62901
former football player

Scammon, Richard
1619 Massachusetts Ave. NW
Washington DC 20036
political scientist specializing in elections research

Scavullo, Francesco
212 E. 63rd St.
New York, NY 10021
photographer

Scheib, Earl
9158 W. Olympic Blvd.
Beverly Hills, CA 90210
world's largest commercial automobile painting company

Scheider, Roy
255 W. 90th St.
New York, NY 10024
actor

Schein, Dr. P.
Georgetown Univ. Hospital
37th & O Sts. NW
Washington, DC 20057
chemotherapy specialist

Scher, John
412 Pleasant Valley Way
West Orange, NJ 07052
rock concert promoter

Schindler, Rabbi Alexander M.
Union of American Hebrew
Congregations
838 5th Ave.
New York, NY 10021
union president

Schlafly, Phyllis
68 Fairmount
Alton, IL 62002
anti-ERA movement leader

Schlesinger, Arthur
City University of New York
33 W. 42nd St.
New York, NY 10036
*special ass't.
to President Kennedy*

Schlesinger, James R.
U.S. Department of Energy
Washington DC 20545
secretary of energy

Schmidt, Alexander
Vice-Chancellor of Health
Services
University of Illinois Medical
Center
414 AOB, P.O. Box 6998
Chicago, IL 60680
former commissioner, FDA

Schmidt, Helmut
Office of the Chancellor
Bonn, West Germany
chancellor of West Germany

Schmitt, Harrison H.
Senate Office Building
Washington DC 20510
senator from New Mexico

Scholl, Art
Rialto Municipal Airport
1700 W. Miro Way
Rialto, CA 92376
movie and stunt pilot

Schorr, Daniel
3113 Woodley Road NW
Washington DC 20008
*radio-TV commentator who
disclosed Pike Report*

Schroeder, Patricia
House Office Building
Washington DC 20515
U.S. representative

Schruefer, Dr. J.J.
Georgetown Univ. Hospital
37th & O Sts. NW
Washington DC 20057
high-risk pregnancy specialist

Schultze, Charles
Council of Economic Advisors
Washington DC 20506
council chairman

Schulz, Charles
c/o United Features Syndicate
200 Park Ave.
New York, NY 10017
cartoonist

Schuster, Joe
c/o Warner Brothers
4000 Warner Blvd.
Burbank, CA 91522
co-creator of Superman

Schwabs Drug Store
8024 Sunset Blvd.
Los Angeles, CA 90046
*Bernard & Leon
Schwab, owners*

Schwarzenegger, Arnold
P.O. Box 1234
Santa Monica, CA 90406
body builder, actor

Schweiker, Richard
Senate Office Building
Washington DC 20510
senator from Pennsylvania

Scott, David
NASA Flight Research
Edwards, CA 93523
astronaut

Scott, Hugh D.
2011 I St. NW
Washington DC 20006
former senator

Scott, Robert W.
Appalachian Regional
Commission
1666 Connecticut Ave. NW
Washington DC 20009
commission co-chairman

Scowcroft, Brent
The White House
Washington DC 20500
*former national security
advisor*

Scranton, William W.
P.O. Box 116
Dalton, PA 18414
former governor

Scribner, Harvey B.
School of Education
University of
Massachusetts
Amherst, MA 01033
*former chancellor of New
York City school system*

Scripps, Edward
Central Trust Tower
Cincinnati, OH 45202
*president, Scripps-Howard
newspapers*

Scruggs, Earl
c/o Columbia Records
51 W. 52nd St.
New York, NY 10019
musician

Scully, Vin
51 W. 52nd St.
New York, NY 10019
sportscaster

Seagrams & Sons
P.O. Box 635
Waterloo, Ontario
Canada H3A 1S9
Joseph Seagrams, president

Seals, Jim
c/o Day 5 Productions
216 Chatsworth Drive
San Fernando, CA 91340
singer, musician

Seamans, Robert C.
Professor of Environment &
Public Policy
Massachusetts Institute of
Technology
50 Memorial Drive
Cambridge, MA 02139
energy expert

Sears, John P. III
718 Falstaff Court
McLean, VA 22101
attorney, political expert

**Sears Roebuck
Company**
Sears Tower
Chicago, IL 60684
Arthur Wood, president

Seaver, Tom
c/o Cincinnati Reds
100 Riverfront Stadium
Cincinnati, OH 45202
baseball player

Sebastian, John
c/o Warner Brothers Records
3300 Warner Blvd.
Burbank, CA 91510
singer, songwriter

Sedaka, Neil
10 Columbus Circle
New York, NY 10019
singer, songwriter

Seeger, Pete
c/o Leventhal
250 W. 57th St.
New York, NY 10019
singer, social activist

Segal, Erich
c/o Dept. of Classics
Yale University
New Haven, CT 06520
*author, educator, long
distance runner*

Segal, George
c/o Lefkowitz Company
1350 6th Ave.
New York, NY 10019
actor

Seger, Bob
c/o Punch Enterprises
567 Purdy St.
Birmingham, MI 48009
musician

Segovia, Andres
c/o Hurok Concerts
1370 Avenue of the Americas
New York, NY 10019
classical guitarist

Segura, Pancho
c/o La Costa Hotel & Spa
Costa del Mar Road
Carlsbad, CA 92075
tennis player

Sellers, Peter
c/o Steinberg, Lipsman Co.
8961 Sunset Blvd.
Los Angeles, CA 90069
actor

Serena
Serena Studios
38 W. 53rd St.
New York, NY 10019
*professional belly dance
instructor*

Serpico, Frank
c/o Ramsey Clark
7 W. 12th St.
New York, NY 10011
*former New York City
police officer*

Sevareid, Eric
c/o CBS News
2020 M St. NW
Washington DC 20036
journalist

Seven-Up Bottling Co.
27 S. Meramec Ave.
St. Louis, MO 63105
Ben Wells, president

Severinson, Doc
c/o Bud Robinson
Productions
100 Alta Loma Road
Los Angeles, CA 90069
trumpet player, band leader

**Sex Information
Council of America**
Palomar Arcade #107
Santa Cruz, CA 95060
Joel Adams, director

Shaklee Company
900 Powell St.
Emeryville, CA 94608
Forrest Shaklee, president

Sha Na Na
c/o Ron Weisner
9200 Sunset Blvd.
Los Angeles, CA 90069
music group

Shange, Ntozake
c/o New York Shakespeare
Festival
425 Lafayette St.
New York, NY 10003
poet, playwright

Shankar, Ravi
6 Pavlova
Little Gibbs Road
Bombay, India
musician

Shapp, Milton
626 S. Bowman Ave.
Merion, PA 19066
former governor

**Shariat-Madari,
Mohammed Kaze**
Tabriz, Iran
*ranking member of Iran's
revolutionary council*

Sharif, Omar
c/o Wm. Morris
151 El Camino Drive
Beverly Hills, CA 90212
actor, bridge player

Sharkman, Bernard
1511 K St. NW Suite 843
Washington DC 20005
*intn'l counsel to the
World Boxing Association*

Sharp, Edward
Sunset Tower South 101
Cape Coral, FL 33904
criminologist

**Sharp, Ulysses
S. Grant**
c/o Teledyne Aero
2701 Harbor Drive
San Diego, CA 92138
*grandson of
Ulysses S. Grant*

Shatner, William
c/o Art Stashower
6399 Wilshire Blvd.
Penthouse
Los Angeles, CA 90048
actor

Shaw, Artie
2123 Outpost Drive
Hollywood, CA 90068
musician, band leader

Sheldon, Sidney
c/o William Morrow & Co.
105 Madison Ave.
New York, NY 10016
author

Shell Oil Company
One Shell Plaza
Houston, TX 77001

Dick de Bruyne, president

Shelton, Robert
P.O. Box 2369
Tuscaloosa, AL 35401
*imperial wizard of
the Ku Klux Klan*

Shepard, Alan B. Jr.
3344 Chevy Chase St. #200
Houston, TX 77019
former astronaut

Shepard, Daniel
67 Kirkland St.
Cambridge, MA 02139
*invented an electronic
warning system to save
porpoises from
commercial fishermen*

Shepherd, Cybill
c/o The Ufland Agency
190 N. Canon Drive
Beverly Hills, CA 90212
actress, model

Shepp, Archie
27 Cooper Square
New York, NY 10003
saxophonist

Sherman Williams Paint Company
101 Prospect Ave. NW
Cleveland, OH 44115
W.O. Spencer, president

Shields & Yarnell
c/o ICM
8899 Beverly Blvd.
Los Angeles, CA 90048
mime team

Shire, Talia
c/o Creative Artists Agency
1888 Century Park East
Suite 1400
Los Angeles, CA 90067
actress

Shlyen, Ben
825 Van Brunt Road
Kansas City, MO 64124
*publisher, Box Office
magazine*

Shockley, William B.
Stanford Electronics
Laboratory
McCullough 202
Stanford University
Stanford, CA 94305
physicist

Shoemaker, Willie
c/o Stilwell Inc.
5900 Wilshire Blvd. #1100
Los Angeles, CA 90036
jockey, sports commentator

Shore, Dinah
c/o KTLA Studios
5800 Sunset Blvd.
Hollywood, CA 90028
singer, talk show hostess

Short, Bobby
c/o Hunt Associates
234 W. 44th St.
New York, NY 10036
entertainer

Shortridge, Stephen
c/o Hanson & Schwam
9229 Sunset Blvd.
Los Angeles, CA 90069
actor

Shriver, Eunice
c/o Kennedy Foundation
1701 K St. NW Suite 203
Washington DC 20006
president, Special Olympics

Shriver, Sargent
600 New Hampshire Ave. NW
Washington DC 20037
*attorney, former
vice-presidential candidate*

Shula, Don
16400-D NW 32nd Ave.
Miami, FL 33054
football coach

Shumway, Dr. N.
Stanford University Hospital
Stanford, CA 94305
*heart surgeon; heart
transplant specialist*

Sidney, George
1140 Tower Road
Beverly Hills, CA 90210
director

Siegel, Jerry
c/o Warner Brothers
4000 Warner Blvd.
Burbank, CA 91522
*co-creator of
Superman character*

Siegel, Stanley
c/o Wm. Morris
1350 Avenue of the Americas
New York, NY 10019
talk show host

Signoret, Simone
15 Place Dauphine
Paris, France
actress

Sikes, Robert L.F.
House Office Building
Washington DC 20515
U.S. representative

Silberg, Dr. D.H.
Hospital of the
University of Pennsylvania
34th & Spruce Sts.
Philadelphia, PA 19104
*neurologist specializing
in multiple sclerosis*

**Silberman,
Laurence H.**
5 Kittery Court
Bethesda, MD 20034
former ambassador

Sills, Beverly
c/o Lustig Management
11 W. 57th St.
New York, NY 10019
*opera singer; artistic
director, New York City Opera*

Silverman, Fred
c/o NBC TV
30 Rockefeller Plaza
New York, NY 10020
president, NBC TV

Silverman, Syd
154 W. 46th St.
New York, NY 10036
publisher, Variety

Silvers, Phil
c/o ICM
8899 Beverly Blvd.
Los Angeles, CA 90048
actor, comedian

**Simmons Mattress
Company**
P.O. Box 49000
Atlanta, GA 30362
Grant Simmons, president

Simon & Schuster
630 5th Ave.
New York, NY 10020
Leon Shimkin, president

Simon, Carly
c/o Rothberg Inc.
850 Devon Ave.
Los Angeles, CA 90024
singer, songwriter

Simon, John
c/o *New York Magazine*
755 2nd Ave.
New York, NY 10017
film and drama critic

Simon, Melvin
260 S. Beverly Drive
Beverly Hills, CA 90212
producer

Simon, Neil
211 S. Beverly Drive
Beverly Hills, CA 90212
playwright

Simon, Norton
411 W. Colorado Blvd.
Los Angeles, CA 90041
industrialist

Simon, Paul
c/o Mort Lewis
11 Bailey Ave.
Ridgefield, CT 06877
singer, songwriter

Simon, William E.
c/o Booz-Allen & Hamilton
245 Park Ave.
New York, NY 10017
*former secretary
of the treasury*

Simone, Nina
c/o Associated Book Corp.
445 Park Ave.
New York, NY 10022
singer, composer

**Simplicity Pattern
Company**
200 Madison Ave.
New York, NY 10016
Harold Cooper, president

Simpson, Allan K.
Senate Office Building
Washington DC 20510
senator from Wyoming

Simpson, O.J.
360 Rockingham
Los Angeles, CA 90049
*actor, sports
commentator, producer*

Simpson, Richard O.
Washington Building
Suite 935
Washington DC 20005
*former chairman, Consumer
Product Safety Commission*

Sinatra, Frank
c/o Samuel Goldwyn Studios
1041 N. Formosa Ave.
Hollywood, CA 90046
singer, actor

Sinatra, Nancy
c/o Sharr
9145 Sunset Blvd. Suite 228
Los Angeles, CA 90069
singer

Singer Sewing Company
30 Rockefeller Plaza
New York, NY 10020
Joseph Flavin, president

Sirhan, Sirhan
Soledad State Prison
Soledad, CA 93960
convicted assassin of Robert F. Kennedy

Sirica, John J.
U.S. Courthouse
Washington DC 20001
Watergate judge, author

Skelton, Red
P.O. Box 136
Anza, CA 92306
entertainer

Slaughter, Enos
R.R. #2
Roxboro, NC 27573
former baseball player

Slayton, Donald K.
Manned Spacecraft
Center NASA
Houston, TX 77058
astronaut

Slick, Grace
2400 Fulton St.
San Francisco, CA 94118
singer

Sloan, Hugh
c/o St. Regis Paper Co.
150 E. 42nd St.
New York, NY 10017
Nixon campaign treasurer

Small Business Administration
1441 L St. NW
Washington DC 20416
Vernon Weaver Jr., administrator

Smeal, Eleanor
425 13th St. NW
Washington DC 20004
president, National Organization for Women

Smith, Alexis
c/o ICM
8899 Beverly Blvd.
Los Angeles, CA 90048
actress

Smith, Buffalo Bob
c/o WQDY
281 Main St.
Calais, ME 04619
creator and host of the "Howdy Doody Show"

Smith, Edmund Law Rogers
230 Stoney Run Lane Apt. 2A
Baltimore, MD 21210
great-great-great-great grandson of Martha Custis Washington (wife of George Washington)

Smith, Howard K.
1124 Connecticut Ave. NW
Washington DC 20036
journalist

Smith, Jaclyn
c/o 20th Century Fox
10201 Pico Blvd.
Los Angeles, CA 90064
actress

Smith, Kate
c/o Katz-Gallin-Morey
Enterprises
9255 Sunset Blvd.
Suite 1115
Los Angeles, CA 90069
singer

Smith, Leon
Beverly Hills Hotel
9641 Sunset Blvd.
Beverly Hills, CA 90210
head doorman

Smith, Liz
160 E. 38th St.
New York, NY 10016
syndicated entertainment columnist

Smith, Maggie
c/o Fraser & Dunlop
91 Regent St.
London WIR 8R0
England
actress

Smith, Margaret Chase
Norridgewock Ave.
Showhegan, ME 04976
former U.S. senator

Smith, Mary Louise
Republican Central
Committee
1540 High St.
Des Moines, IA 50309
*former chairperson,
Republican National
Committee*

Smith, Patti
c/o Wartoke Concern
1545 Broadway
New York, NY 10036
singer

Smith, Preston E.
4089 Club House Road
Loropoe, CA 93436
former governor of Texas

Smith, Red
228 W. 43rd St.
New York, NY 10036
sports columnist

Smith, Richard
209 Murray Ave.
Larchmont, NY 10538
*make-up artist who founded
make-up department at NBC*

Mrs. Smith's Pie Co.
South & Charlotte Sts.
Pottstown, PA 19464
Robert S. Smith, president

Smith, Robyn
Belmont, NY 11003
*first female jockey to
win major stakes race*

Smith, Stan
888 17th St. NW Suite 1200
Washington DC 20006
tennis player

Smokey the Bear
Forest Service
Department of Agriculture
The Mall between 12th
& 14th Sts. NW
Washington DC 20250
fire prevention mascot

Smothers, Dick & Tom
260 S. Beverly Drive
Beverly Hills, CA 90212
comedians

Snead, Sam
c/o Uni-Managers
10880 Wilshire Blvd.
Los Angeles, CA 90024
golfer

Snelling, Richard A.
Office of the Governor
Montpelier, VT 05602
governor of Vermont

Snodgress, Carrie
c/o Century Artists
9744 Wilshire Blvd.
Beverly Hills, CA 90212
actress

Snoopy
c/o United
Features Syndicate
200 Park Ave.
New York, NY 10017
comic strip character

Snow, Hank
P.O. Box 1084
Nashville, TN 37202
entertainer

Snow, Phoebe
c/o Bernstein
505 Park Ave.
New York, NY 10022
singer, songwriter

Snyder, Jimmy "the Greek"
255 Alhambra Circle
Coral Gables, FL 33134
oddsmaker

Snyder, Tom
c/o NBC TV
30 Rockefeller Plaza
New York, NY 10020
talk show host

Society for Iranian Studies
P.O. Box K-154
Boston College
Boston, MA 01432
Dr. Lois Beck, secretary

Solanas, Valerie
170 E. 3rd St.
New York, NY 10009
*would-be assassin of
Andy Warhol*

Solar Energy Construction Association
404 W. Campbell Ave.
Roanoake, VA 24014
Howard D. Wolfe, founder

Solti, Sir Georg
c/o Chicago Symphony
Orchestra
220 S. Michigan Ave.
Chicago, IL 60604
conductor

Solzhenitsyn, Alexsander
c/o Harper & Row Publishers
10 E. 53rd St.
New York, NY 10022
Soviet dissident, author

Somers, Suzanne
c/o Jay Bernstein
9110 Sunset Blvd.
Los Angeles, CA 90069
actress

Sommer, Elke
c/o Contemporary-Korman
Artists
132 Lasky Drive
Beverly Hills, CA 90212
actress

Sondheim, Stephen J.
246 E. 49th St.
New York, NY 10017
composer, lyricist

Sonnenfeldt, Helmut
4105 Thornapple St.
Chevy Chase, MD 20015
*former state department
official*

Sorensen, Theodore
345 Park Ave.
New York, NY 10022
*former special counsel to
the president*

Sothern, Ann
c/o Contemporary-Korman
Artists
132 Lasky Drive
Beverly Hills, CA 90212
actress

Soul, David
c/o Sharr
9145 Sunset Blvd. Suite 228
Los Angeles, CA 90069
actor

Spacek, Sissy
c/o Wm. Morris
1350 Avenue of the Americas
New York, NY 10019
actress

Spahn, Warren
R.R. 2
Hurtshone, OK 74547
*member of baseball Hall
of Fame*

Spann, Gloria
Plains, GA 31780
sister of Jimmy Carter

Speck, Richard
Joliet Correctional Center
Cell 225
Joliet, IL 60438
mass murderer

Spector, Phil
P.O. Box 69529
Los Angeles, CA 90069
record producer

Spelling, Aaron
c/o 20th Century Fox
10201 Pico Blvd.
Los Angeles, CA 90064
producer

Spencer, Dr. F.C.
New York University
550 1st Ave.
New York, NY 10016
heart surgeon

Spiderman
c/o Marvel Comics
575 Madison Ave.
New York, NY 10022
superhero

Spiegel Company
175 E. Delaware Place
Chicago, IL 60611
Modie Spiegel, president

Spinks, Leon
c/o World Boxing
Association
1511 K St. NW Suite 843
Washington DC 20005
*former world heavyweight
boxing champion*

Spitz, Mark
c/o Wm. Morris
151 El Camino Drive
Beverly Hills, CA 90212
swimmer, sports commentator

Spivak, Lawrence
2660 Woodley Road NW
Washington DC 20008
creator of "Meet the Press"

Spock, Dr. Benjamin
P.O. Box N
Rogers, AZ 72756
author, anti-war activist

Springsteen, Bruce
c/o Columbia Records
51 W. 52nd St.
New York, NY 10019
singer, songwriter

Squibb Company
40 W. 57th St.
New York, NY 10019
Richard Furland, president

Squires, Dick
7 Pond St.
Rowayton, CT 06883
*platform tennis champion
and instructor*

Staats, Elmer B.
General Accounting Office
441 G St.
Washington DC 20548
U.S. comptroller general

Stabler, Ken
7811 Oakport St.
Oakland, CA 94621
football player

Stack, Robert
St. Pierre Road
Los Angeles, CA 90024
actor

Stafford, Robert T.
Senate Office Building
Washington DC 20510
senator from Vermont

Stafford, Thomas
c/o USAF
Flight Test Center
Edwards Air Force Base
Edwards, CA 93523
astronaut

Stallone, Sylvester
c/o Jeff Wald Associates
9356 Santa Monica Blvd.
Beverly Hills, CA 90210
actor

Stanley, Oren
720 Davis Ave.
Corning, IA 50841
*president, National Farmers
Organization*

**Standard & Poors
Company**
345 Hudson St.
New York, NY 10014
Frederich Stahl, president

Stans, Maurice H.
5114 N. 40th St.
Phoenix, AZ 85018
*chief fund raiser for Nixon
campaign*

Stanwyck, Barbara
c/o Wm. Morris
151 El Camino Drive
Beverly Hills, CA 90212
actress

Stapleton, Jean
c/o Arcara, Bauman & Heller
Artists Management
9220 Sunset Blvd.
Los Angeles, CA 90069
actress

Stapleton, Maureen
c/o ICM
8899 Beverly Blvd.
Los Angeles, CA 90048
actress

Stark, Ray
Rastar Productions
300 Colgems Square
Burbank, CA 91505
producer

Starr, Bart
1265 Lombardi Ave.
Green Bay, WI 54303
football coach

Starr, Ringo
Ring O'Records
17 Berkeley St.
London W1, England
drummer, singer

Staubach, Roger
c/o Dallas Cowboys
6116 W. Central Expressway
Dallas, TX 75206
football player

Steiger, Rod
c/o ICM
8899 Beverly Blvd.
Los Angeles, CA 90048
actor

Stein, Gertrude
133 N. Lowry Ave.
Springfield, OH 45504
educator, author

Stein, Herbert
1704 Yorktown Drive
Charlottesville, VA 22901
economist

Stein, Dr. Jules
P.O. Box 30
Beverly Hills, CA 90213
*founder, Music Corporation
of America (MCA)*

Steinberg, David
c/o Wm. Morris
151 El Camino Drive
Beverly Hills, CA 90212
comedian

Steinbrenner, George M. III
American Shipbuilding Co.
Bond Court Building
Suite 911
1300 E. 9th St.
Cleveland, OH 44114
business executive, owner of N.Y. Yankees

Steinem, Gloria
370 Lexington Ave.
New York, NY 10017
leader of women's liberation movement

Steinway Piano Co.
Steinway Place
Long Island City, NY 11105
Henry Steinway, president

Stennis, John C.
Senate Office Building
Washington DC 20510
senator from Mississippi

Stern, Isaac
c/o ICM
40 W. 57th St.
New York, NY 10019
violinist

Stern, Leonard
Heyday Productions
c/o Columbia Pictures
Colgems Square Suite 1055
Burbank, CA 91505
producer, writer, director

Stevens, Cat
c/o BKM
9200 Sunset Blvd.
Los Angeles, CA 90069
singer, songwriter

Stevens, Connie
c/o Styne Company
148 S. Beverly Drive
Beverly Hills, CA 90212
entertainer, actress

Stevens, George Jr.
Kennedy Center
Washington DC 20566
motion picture executive

Stevens, John Paul
U.S. Supreme Court
Washington DC 20543
justice

Stevens, Ray
Ahab Music
1707 Grand Ave.
Nashville, TN 37212
singer, songwriter

Stevens, Roger L.
John F. Kennedy Center for the Performing Arts
Washington DC 20506
producer

Stevens, Theodore
Senate Office Building
Washington DC 20510
senator from Alaska

Stevenson, Adlai Ewing III
Senate Office Building
Washington DC 20510
senator from Illinois

Stevenson, McLean
c/o Wm. Morris
151 El Camino Drive
Beverly Hills, CA 90212
actor

Stevenson, Parker
c/o Wm. Morris
151 El Camino Drive
Beverly Hills, CA 90212
actor

Stewart, Donald W.
Senate Office Building
Washington DC 20510
senator from Alabama

Stewart, Jackie
International Management
2 Erieview Plaza
Cleveland, OH 44114
retired race driver, sports commentator

Stewart, Jimmy
c/o Chasin-Park-Citron
9255 Sunset Blvd.
Los Angeles, CA 90069
actor

Stewart, Mary
c/o Fawcett Publications
1515 Broadway
New York, NY 10036
author

Stewart, Potter
U.S. Supreme Court
Washington DC 20543
justice

Stewart, Rod
c/o Graff Music
1245 N. Doheny Drive
Los Angeles, CA 90069
singer

Stiller, Jerry
c/o Morgan Communication
250 W. 57th St.
New York, NY 10019
comedian

Stills, Stephen
c/o Gold Hill Management
P.O. Box 4008
Boulder, CO 80302
singer

Stokes, Carl
c/o WNBC TV
30 Rockefeller Plaza
New York, NY 10020
former mayor of Cleveland

Stokes, Louis
House Office Building
Washington DC 20515
U.S. representative

Stolley, Richard
Time-Life Building
Rockefeller Plaza
New York, NY 10020
*managing editor of
People Magazine*

Stone, Albert
P.O. Box 8427
Louisville, KY 40208
president, Churchill Downs

Stone, I.F.
4420 29th St. NW
Washington DC 20008
journalist

Stone, Richard B.
Senate Office Building
Washington DC 20510
senator from Florida

Stone, W. Clement
222 W. Adams St.Chicago,
Chicago, IL 60606
*businessman, campaign
financier*

Strachan, Gordon C.
Kearns Building
Salt Lake City, UT 84222
former aide to H.R. Haldeman

Strasberg Lee
135 Central Park W.
New York, NY 10023
drama coach, actor

Strasberg, Susan
c/o Kemp Management
1901 Avenue of the Stars
Suite 465
Los Angeles, CA 90067
actress

Strauss, Peter
c/o Wm. Morris
1350 Avenue of the Americas
New York, NY 10019
actor

Strauss, Robert S.
Executive Office of the
President
1800 G St. NW Suite 719
Washington DC 20506
*trade negotiator, former
Democratic National
Committee chairman*

Strassman, Marcia
c/o APA
9000 Sunset Blvd.
Los Angeles, CA 90069
actress

Streep, Meryl
c/o ICM
40 W. 57th St.
New York, NY 10019
actress

Streisand, Barbra
c/o First Artists Productions
Burbank Studios
Burbank, CA 91522
singer, actress

Strong, Leonell
11661 Sorrento Valley Road
San Diego, CA 92121
cancer research scientist

Stroup, Keith
2317 M St. NW
Washington DC 20037
*director, National Organiza-
tion for the Reform of
Marijuana Laws*

Struthers, Sally
c/o Creative Artists Agency
1888 Century Park E.
Suite 1400
Los Angeles, CA 90067
actress

Stryon, William
c/o Random House
201 E. 50th St.
New York, NY 10022
author

Stuart, Jesse
West Hollow
Greenup, KY 41144
author

Studio 54
254 W. 54th St.
New York, NY 10019
Steve Rubell, owner

Sturgis, Frank
c/o Henry B. Rothblatt
232 West End Ave.
New York, NY 10023
convicted Watergate burglar

Styne, Jule
237 W. 57th St.
New York, NY 10019
composer, producer

Styx
c/o Jim Cahill
P.O. Box 27091
Los Feliz Station
Los Angeles, CA 90027
music group

Sullivan, William B.
U.S. State Department
Washington DC 20520
ambassador to Iran

Sulzberger, Arthur Ochs
c/o *New York Times*
229 W. 43rd St.
New York, NY 10036
publisher

Summer, Donna
c/o Casablanca Records &
FilmWorks
8255 Sunset Blvd.
Los Angeles, CA 90046
singer

Supertramp
c/o A&M Records
1416 N. La Brea Ave.
Hollywood, CA 90028
music group

Susskind, David
747 3rd Ave.
New York, NY 10017
producer

Sutherland, Donald
c/o Wm. Morris
151 El Camino Drive
Beverly Hills, CA 90212
actor

Swan, Billy
35 Music Square
Nashville, TN 37203
musician

Swanson, Gloria
920 5th Ave.
New York, NY 10021
actress

Swayze, John Cameron
491 Riversville Road
Greenwich, CT 06830
journalist

Sweet, John
2300 N St. NW
Washington DC 20037
*publisher, U.S. News &
World Report*

Swit, Loretta
c/o Sharr
9145 Sunset Blvd. Suite 228
Los Angeles, CA 90069
actress

Symington, Stuart
1700 K St. NW Suite 400
Washington DC 20006
former senator

Synanon Foundation
6055 Marshall-Petaluma Road
P.O. Box 786
Marshall, CA 94940
*Charles E. Dederich,
chairman of the board*

Szabo, Gabor
7250 Franklin Ave.
Los Angeles, CA 90046
guitarist, composer

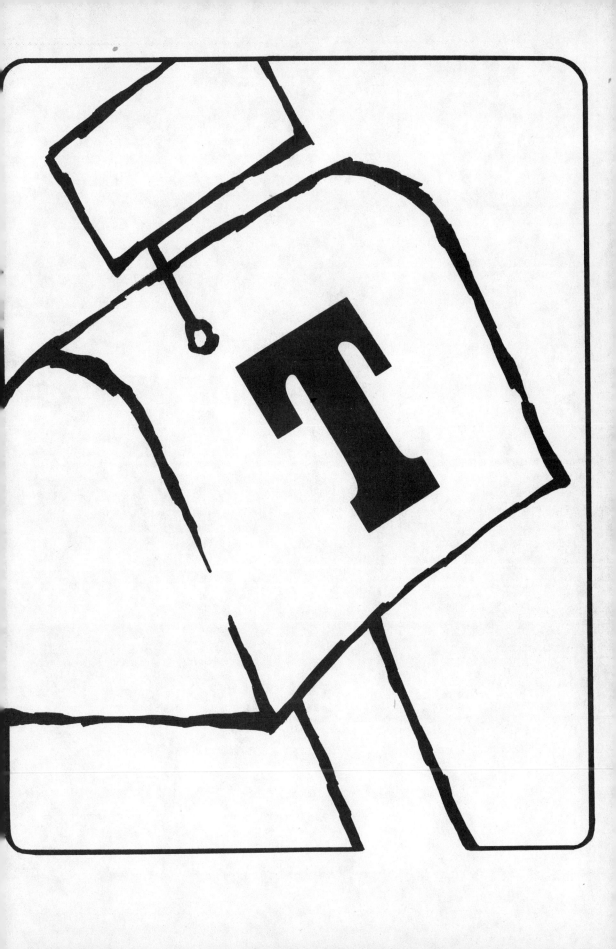

TRW Credit Checking Co.
23555 Euclid Ave.
Cleveland, OH 44117
R.F. Mettler, president

Taft, Charles
1071 Celestial St.
Cincinnati, OH 45202
attorney, son of William Howard Taft

Taft, Robert A. Jr.
4300 Drake Road
Cincinnati, OH 45243
former U.S. senator

Talese, Gay
154 E. Atlantic Blvd.
Ocean City, NJ 08226
writer

Talmadge, Herman E.
Senate Office Building
Washington DC 20510
senator from Georgia

Tamboro, Fred
220 Woodcliff Ave.
North Bergen, NJ 07047
leader of the "Hoboken Four" the first singing group Frank Sinatra belonged to

Tampax Company
5 Dakota Drive
Lake Success, NY 10040
T.F. Casey, president

Tanner, Roscoe
1109 Gnome Trail
Lookout Mountain, TN 37350
tennis player

Tarkenton, Fran
c/o NBC Sports
30 Rockefeller Plaza
New York, NY 10020
sportscaster, retired football player

Tarnower, Herman
c/o Bantam Books
666 5th Ave.
New York, NY 10016
diet specialist, author of Scarsdale diet

Tastebuds
c/o Anheuser-Busch
721 Pestalozzi St.
St. Louis, MO 63118
mascot used in Budweiser commercials

Taupin, Bernie
c/o John Reid Enterprises
211 S. Beverly Drive #200
Beverly Hills, Ca 90212
lyricist

Tayback, Vic
c/o CBS TV
7800 Beverly Blvd.
Los Angeles, CA 90036
actor

Taylor, Elizabeth
P.O. Box 1320
Middleburg, VA 22117
actress

Taylor, James
644 N. Doheny Drive
Los Angeles, CA 90069
singer, songwriter

Taylor, Rip
c/o Chuck Barris Productions
6430 Sunset Blvd.
Hollywood, CA 90028
comedian

Taylor, Ron & Valerie
Sea & Sea Travel Service
680 Beach St. Suite 340
Wharfside
San Francisco, CA 94109
underwater film-makers

Teasdale, Joseph P.
Office of the Governor
Jefferson City, MO 65101
governor of Missouri

Teeawen, Gustaaf
P.O. Box 37198
Overport, Durban
Republic of South Africa
expert on jungle sounds

Telephone Companies:

American Telephone & Telegraph Co.
195 Broadway
New York, NY 10007
John deButts, president

Bell Canada
1050 Beaver Hall Hill
Montreal, Canada H3C 3G4
A.J. deGrandpre, president

Bell Telephone Co. of Pennsylvania
1 Parkway
Philadelphia, PA 19102
William L. Mobraaten, president

Chesapeake & Potomac Telephone Company
1710 H St. NW
Washington DC 20006
Samuel E. Bonsack, president

Chesapeake & Potomac of Maryland
320 St. Paul Place
Baltimore, MD 21202
Thomas M. Gibbons, president

Chesapeake & Potomac of Virginia
703 E. Grace St.
Richmond, VA 23219
Lee C. Trait, president

Chesapeake & Potomac of West Virginia
1500 MacCorkle Ave. S.E.
Charleston, WV 25314
Frank R. Hoffman, president

Cincinnati Bell
225 E. 4th St.
Cincinnati, OH 45202
Richard T. Dugan, president

Diamond State Telephone Co.
3900 Washington St.
Wilmington, DE 19802
Joseph F. Hulihan, president

Illinois Bell Telephone Co.
225 West Randolph St.
Chicago, IL 60606
Charles Marshall, president

Indiana Bell Telephone Co.
240 North Meridian St.
Indianapolis, IN 46204
Delbert C. Staley, president

Michigan Bell Telephone Co.
444 Michigan Ave.
Detroit, MI 48226
David K. Easlick, president

Mountain States Telephone
931 14th St.
Denver, CO 80202
Robert K. Timothy, president

New England Telephone
185 Franklin St.
Boston, MA 02107
William C. Mercer, president

New Jersey Bell Telephone
540 Broad St.
Newark, NJ 07101
Robert W. Kleinert, president

New York Telephone Co.
1095 Avenue of the Americas
New York, NY 10036
John R. Mulhearn, president

Northwestern Bell Telephone Co.
100 S. 19th St.
Omaha, NE 68102
Jack A. MacAllister, president

Ohio Bell Telephone
100 Erieview Plaza
Cleveland, OH 44114
Charles E. Hugel, president

Pacific Telephone
140 New Montgomery St.
San Francisco, CA 94105
Gordon Hough, president

Pacific Northwest Bell Telephone Co.
1600 Bell Plaza
Seattle, WA 98191
Wallace R. Bunn, president

South Central Bell Telephone Co.
Headquarters Bldg.
P.O. Box 771
Birmingham, AL 35201
W. Cecil Bauer, president

Southern Bell Telephone
Hurt Bldg.
P.O. Box 2211
Atlanta, GA 30301
L. Edmund Rast, president

Southern New England Telephone Co.
227 Church St.
New Haven, CT 06506
Alfred W. VanSinderen, president

Southwestern Bell Telephone Co.
1010 Pine St.
St. Louis, MO 63101
Zane E. Barnes, president

Wisconsin Telephone Co.
722 N. Broadway
Milwaukee, WI 53202
Gustave H. Moede, Jr., president

Teller, Dr. Edward
Hoover Institute On War,
Resolution & Peace
Stanford, CA 94305
senior research fellow; father of the H-bomb

Teresa, Mother
Mission of Charity
Calcutta, India
mission founder, 1979 Nobel Peace Prize winner

Ter Horst, Jerald
511 National Press Building
Washington DC 20004
press secretary to former President Ford

Terrio, Deney
1541 N. Vine St.
Hollywood, CA 90028
dancer who taught John Travolta for "Saturday Night Fever"

Texaco
2000 Westchester Ave.
White Plains, NY 10650
Maurice Granville, president

Tharp, Twyla
137 Riverside Drive
New York, NY 10024
dancer, choreographer

Thatcher, Margaret
10 Downing St.
London, England
prime minister of England

Thomas, B.J.
P.O. Box 1569
Fayetteville, NC 28301
singer, songwriter

Thomas, Danny
c/o Wm. Morris
151 El Camino Drive
Beverly Hills, CA 90212
entertainer, actor

Thomas, Lowell
Hammersley Hill
Pawling, NY 12564
broadcast commentator, author

Thomas, Marlo
P.O. Box 663
Beverly Hills, CA 90213
actress

Thomas, Richard
c/o ICPR
9255 Sunset Blvd.
Los Angeles, CA 90069
actor

Thompson, Hank
3224 S. Norwood Ave.
Tulsa, OK 74135
entertainer

Thompson, James R.
Office of the Governor
State Capitol
Springfield, IL 62706
governor of Illinois

Thompson, Sada
P.O. Box 547
Jackson Heights, NY 11372
actress

Thompson, Virgil
222 W. 23rd St.
New York, NY 10011
composer, music critic

Thone, Charles
Office of the Governor
Lincoln, NE 68509
governor of Nebraska

Thornburgh, Richard L.
Office of the Governor
State Capitol
Harrisburg, PA 17102
governor of Pennsylvania

Thornton, William
Manned Spacecraft Center
NASA
Houston, TX 77058
astronaut

Thurmond, Nate
2923 Streetsboro Road
Richfield, OH 44286
basketball player

Thurmond, Strom
Senate Office Building
Washington DC 20510
senator from South Carolina

Tiant, Luis
Hallen Ave.
Milton, MA 02186
baseball player

Tiegs, Cheryl
1130 5th Ave.
New York, NY 10028
model

Tierney, Gene
9644 Heather Road
Beverly Hills, CA 90210
actress

Tillis, Mel
5800 E. Shelly Drive
Penthouse
Tulsa, OK 74135
singer

Timex Watch Co.
Timex Corporation
Waterbury, CT 06720
Martin Siem, president

Tinker, Grant
c/o CBS Studios
4024 Radford Ave.
Studio City, CA 91604
producer

Tinling, Ted
147 N. 12th St.
Philadelphia, PA 19107
*ladies' tennis
clothes designer*

Tippers Anonymous
P.O. Box 178
Cochitvate, MA 01778
*group dedicated to tipping
only when service is
exceptional; Robert
Farrington, president*

Tito, Marshal
Office of the President
Belgrade, Yugoslavia
president of Yugoslavia

Tkach, Maj. Gen. Walter R.
Air Force Systems Command
Andrews Air Force Base
Washington DC 20335
surgeon

Toffler, Alvin
Washington, CT 06793
author

Toland, John
1 Long Ridge Road
Danbury, CT 06810
author, historian

Tomlin, Lily
P.O. Box 69330
Los Angeles, CA 90069
comedienne, actress

"Tonight Show"
3000 W. Alameda
Burbank, CA 91523
*Shirley Woods,
talent coordinator*

Tonka Toy Company
10505 Wayzata Blvd.
Hopkins, MN 55343
Peter Wimsatt, president

Tony the Tiger
c/o Kellogg Company
235 Porter St.
Battle Creek, MI 49016
corn flakes mascot

Topps Chewing Gum Company
254 36th St.
Brooklyn, NY 11232
Joel Shorin, president

Torme, Mel
c/o ICM
8899 Beverly Blvd.
Los Angeles, CA 90048
singer

Torrijos, Gen. Omar
Panama City, Panama
*general of Republic
of Panama*

Tower, John G.
Senate Office Building
Washington DC 20510
senator from Texas

Townshend, Peter
c/o Sir Productions
130 W. 57th St.
New York, NY 10019
*musician, leader
of The Who*

Toyota Car Company
1 Toyota cho
Toyota-Shi
Aichi, Japan
Eija Toyoda, president

Tracy, Dick
220 E. 42nd St.
New York, NY 10017
comic strip character

Trans World Airlines
605 3rd Ave.
New York, NY 10016
L.E. Smart, president

Travolta, John
c/o LeMond-Zetter
5160 Genesta Ave.
Encino, CA 91316
actor

Treen, Dave
Office of the Governor
Baton Rouge, LA 70804
governor of Louisiana

Trevino, Lee
P.O. Drawer 12727
El Paso, TX 79912
golfer

Trilateral Commission
345 E. 46th St.
New York, NY 10017
George S. Franklin, coordinator

Trudeau, Margaret
c/o Paddington
Publishing Co.
925 Madison Ave.
New York, NY 10016
estranged wife of Canadian prime minister

Trudeau, Pierre
24 Sussex Drive
Ottawa, Ontario
Canada
prime minister of Canada

Truffaut, Francois
5 Rue Robert-Estienne
Paris 8e, France
film director

Truman, Bess
219 N. Delaware St.
Independence, MO 64105
widow of Harry S. Truman

Truman, Margaret
c/o Morrow & Company
105 Madison Ave.
New York, NY 10016
author; daughter of late Harry S. Truman

Trumbo, Dalton
8710 St. Ives Drive
Los Angeles, CA 90069
playwright, novelist

Tryon, Tom
c/o Fawcett Publications
1515 Broadway
New York, NY 10036
author

Tsongas, Paul
Senate Office Building
Washington DC 20510
senator from Massachusetts

Tucher, Lenn
2020 M St. NW
Washington DC 90069
journalist

Tuchman, Barbara W.
c/o Russell & Volkening
551 5th Ave.
New York, NY 10017
author

Tucker, Tanya
2311 Biscayne Drive #140
Little Rock, AR 72202
singer

Tull, Jethro
c/o Friday Management Ltd.
Road Town, Tortolla
British Virgin Islands 43352
music group

Tunney, John V.
Manatt, Phelps, Rothenberg,
Manley & Tunney
1888 Century Park E.
Los Angeles, CA 90067
former senator

Turkel, Ann
c/o Creative Artists Agency
1888 Century Park E.
Suite 1400
Los Angeles, CA 90067
actress

Turner, Glenn W.
P.O. Box 52, Route 1
Maitland, FL 32751
promoter of "pyramid" schemes

Turner, Ike & Tina
1310 S. La Brea Ave.
Inglewood, CA 90302
singers

Turner, Lana
c/o David Shapira
& Associates
9100 Wilshire Blvd. #231
Beverly Hills, CA 90210
actress

Turner, Stansfield
CIA
Washington DC 20505
CIA director

Tuthill, Harold
130 NW 79th St.
Miami, FL 33150
directs expert witnesses for use in trials

Tuttle, Lyle
30 7th St.
San Francisco, CA 94103
tattoo artist

Twitty, Conway
394 W. Main St. #C-16
Hendersonville, TN 37075
entertainer

Tynan, Kenneth
c/o Simon & Schuster
630 5th Ave.
New York, NY 10020
author

Tyson, Cicely
c/o Wm. Morris
151 El Camino Drive
Beverly Hills, CA 90212
actress

U.S. Chess Federation
186 Route 9W
New Windsor, NY 12550
Martin E. Morrison, executive director

U.S. Hang Gliding Association
P.O. Box 66306
Los Angeles, CA 90006
Lloyd Licher, director

U.S. Industries
250 Park Ave.
New York, NY 10017
John I. Bellara, president

U.S. Olympic Committee
1750 E. Boulder St.
Colorado Springs, CO 80909
Don F. Miller, director

U.S. Parachute Association
15th St. NW Suite 444
Washington DC 20005
William H. Ottley, director

U.S. Steel
600 Grant St.
Pittsburgh, PA 15230
Edgar B. Speer, president

U.S. Tennis Association
51 E. 42nd St.
New York, NY 10017
Michael J. Burns, director

U.S. Touch & Flag Football Association
2705 Normandy Drive
Youngstown, OH 44511
John Kovach, commissioner

Ubell, Earl
30 Rockefeller Plaza
New York, NY 10020
television news producer

Udall, Morris K.
House Office Building
Washington DC 20515
U.S. representative

Udall, Stewart L.
1775 Pennsylvania Ave. NW
Washington DC 20006
former secretary of the interior

Uggams, Leslie
c/o Lewis Co.
8560 Sunset Blvd. #605
Los Angeles, CA 90069
singer, actress

Uglies Unlimited
1714 Merrimac Terrace
Garland, TX 75043
*fights discrimination against uncomely people;
Danny McCoy, founder*

Ullman, Al
House Office Building
Washington DC 20515
U.S. representative

Ullman, Liv
c/o Paul Kohner-Michael Levy Agency
9169 Sunset Blvd.
Los Angeles, CA 90069
actress

Ultman, Dr. J.
University of Chicago Hospitals
Chicago, IL 60612
specialist in Hodgkin's Disease

Unger, Garry
5700 Oakland Ave.
St. Louis, MO 63110
hockey player

Union of Concerned Scientists
1208 Massachusetts Ave.
Cambridge, MA 02138
*anti-nuclear group;
Daniel F. Ford, director*

Unitas, Johnny
600 N. Howard St.
Baltimore, MD 21201
sports commentator

United Airlines
P.O. Box 66100
O'Hare Field
Chicago, IL 60666
Richard J. Ferris, president

Unruh, Jesse M.
915 Capitol Mall – Room 110
Sacramento, CA 95814
government official

Unser, Al
c/o Jim Hall Racing
Route 1, P.O. Box 62
Midland, TX 79701
auto racer

Unser, Bobby
c/o United States Auto Club
4910 W. 16th St.
Speedway, IN 46224
auto racer

Updike, John
c/o Knopf Publishers
201 E. 50th St.
New York, NY 10022
author

Urban, Dr. J.
Memorial Sloan-Kettering
Hospital
New York, NY 10021
surgeon specializing in breast cancer surgery

Urich, Robert
c/o L. Frank & Co.
1801 Avenue of the Stars
Los Angeles, CA 90067
actor

Usery, W.J. Jr.
2400 Virginia Ave.
Washington DC 20037
former secretary of labor

Ustinov, Peter
c/o Mann Ltd.
140 Park Lane
London W1, England
actor

Utility Commissions

National Association of Regulatory Utility Commissioners
1102 Interstate Commerce
Commission Building
Washington DC 20044
Ralph H. Wickbers, president

Alabama Public Service Commission
P.O. Box 991
Montgomery, AL 36102
Kenneth Hammond, president

Alaska Public Utilities Commission
1100 MacKay Building
338 Denail St.
Anchorage, AK 99501
Gordon J. Zerbetz, president

Arizona Corporation
Capitol Annex Building
Phoenix, AZ 85007
Al Faron, president

Arkansas Public Service Commission
Justice Building
Little Rock, AR 72201
Pat Moran, president

California Public Utilities Commission
California State Bldg.
350 McAllister St.
San Francisco, CA 94102
Vernon L. Sturgeon, president

Colorado Public Utilities Commission
500 Columbine Building
1845 Sherman St.
Denver, CO 80203
Edwin R. Lundborg, president

Connecticut Public Utilities Commission
State Office Building
Hartford, Ct 06115
Howard E. Hausman, president

Delaware Public Service Commission
Dover, DE 19901
Curtis W. Steen Sr., president

District of Columbia Public Service Commission
Room 204, Cafritz Building
1625 I St. NW
Washington DC 20006
William R. Stratton, president

Federal Power Commission
825 N. Capitol St. NE
Washington DC 20426
John N. Nassikas, president

Florida Public Service Commission
Whitfield Building
700 S. Adams St.
Tallahassee, FL 32304
William T. Mayo, president

Georgia Public Service Commission
244 Washington St. SW
Atlanta, GA 30334
Ben T. Wiggins, president

Hawaii Public Utilities Commission
P.O. Box 541
Honolulu, HI 96809
Lorrin W. Dolim, president

Idaho Public Utilities Commission
State House
472 W. Washington St.
Boise, ID 83720
Robert Lenaghen, president

Illinois Commerce Commission
527 E. Capitol Ave.
Springfield, IL 62706
Marvin S. Lieberman, president

Indiana Public Service Commission
901 State Office Building
Indianapolis, IN 46204
L.J. Wallace, president

Iowa Commerce Commission
Des Moines, IA 50319
Maurice Van Nostrand, president

Kansas State Corporation Commission
Topeka, KS 66612
Dale E. Saffels, president

Kentucky Public Service Commission
Frankfort, KY 40601
William A. Logan, president

Louisiana Public Service Commission
1 American Place Suite 1630
Baton Rouge, LA 70825
N.B. Knight Jr., president

Maine Public Utilities Commission
Augusta, ME 04330
P.A. Bradford, president

Maryland Public Service Commission
904 State Office Building
301 W. Preston
Baltimore, MD 21201
Robert L. Sullivan Jr., president

Massachusetts Dept. of Public Utilities
Leverett Saltonstall Bldg.
100 Cambridge St.
Boston, MA 02202
Harold Keokane, president

Michigan Public Service Commission
Law Building 5th Floor
525 W. Ottawa St.
Lansing, MI 48913
William G. Rosenberg, president

Minnesota Dept. of Public Service
American Center Building
160 E. Kellogg Blvd.
St. Paul, MN 55101
Karl F. Rolvaag, president

Mississippi Public Service Commission
P.O. Box 1174
Jackson, MS 39205
Norman A. Johnson Jr., president

Missouri Public Service Commission
P.O. Box 360
Jefferson City, MO 65101
James F. Mauze, president

Montana Public Service Commission
1227 11th Ave.
Helena, MT 59601
Gordon E. Bollinger, president

Nebraska State Railway Commission
1342 M St.
Lincoln, NE 68508
John W. Swanson, president

Nevada Public Service Commission
Carson City, NV 89701
Noel A. Clark, president

New Hampshire Public Utilities Commission
Concord, NH 03301
Alexander J. Kalinski, president

New Jersey Dept. of Public Utilities
101 Commerce St.
Newark, NJ 07102
Anthony J. Grossi, president

New Mexico Public Service Commission
Bataan Memorial Building
Sante Fe, NM 87501
Richard P. Montoya, president

New York State Public Service Commission
44 Holland Ave.
Albany, NY 12208
Alfred C. Kahn, president

North Carolina Utilities Commission
Raleigh, NC 27601
Marvin R. Wooten, president

North Dakota Public Service Commission
Bismark, ND 58501
Richard A. Elkins, president

Ohio Public Utilities Commission
111 N. High St.
Columbus, OH 43215
C. Luther Heckman, president

Oklahoma Corp. Commission
Jim Thorpe Office Building
Oklahoma City, OK 73105
Charles Nesbitt, president

Oregon Public Utilities Commissioner
200 Public Service Bldg.
Salem, OR 97310
Richard W. Sabin, commissioner

Pennsylvania Public Utility Commission
P.O. Box 3265
North Officer Building
Harrisburg, PA 17120
Louis J. Carter, president

Rhode Island Public Utilities Commission
169 Weybosset St.
Providence, RI 02903
William Harsch, president

South Carolina Public Service Commission
P.O. Drawer 11649
Columbia, SC 29211
Abney A. Smith, president

South Dakota Public Utilities Commission
Pierre, SD 57501
Normal Klinkel, president

Tennessee Public Service Commission
C1-102 Cordell Hull Building
Nashville, TN 37219
C.L. Pentecost, president

Texas Railroad Commission, Utilities Division
Ernest O. Thompson Building
11th Floor
Austin, TX 78701
Ben Ramsey, president

Utah Public Service Commission
330 E. 4th South St.
Salt Lake City, UT 84111
Frank S. Warner, president

Vermont Public Service Board
7 School St.
Montpelier, VT 05602
M.K. Miller, president

Virginia State Corp. Commission
Blanton Building Box 1197
Richmond, VA 23219
T.P. Harwood Jr., president

**Washington Utilities
& Transportation
Commission**
Highway-Licenses Building
Olympia, WA 98504
Donald H. Brazier, president

**West Virginia Public
Service Commission**
Capitol Building
Charleston, WV 25305
B.E. Smith, president

**Wisconsin Public
Service Commission**
Hill Farms State Office Bldg.
Madison, WI 53702
R.D. Cudahy, president

**Wyoming Public
Service Commission**
Cheyenne, WY 82002
Zan Lewis, president

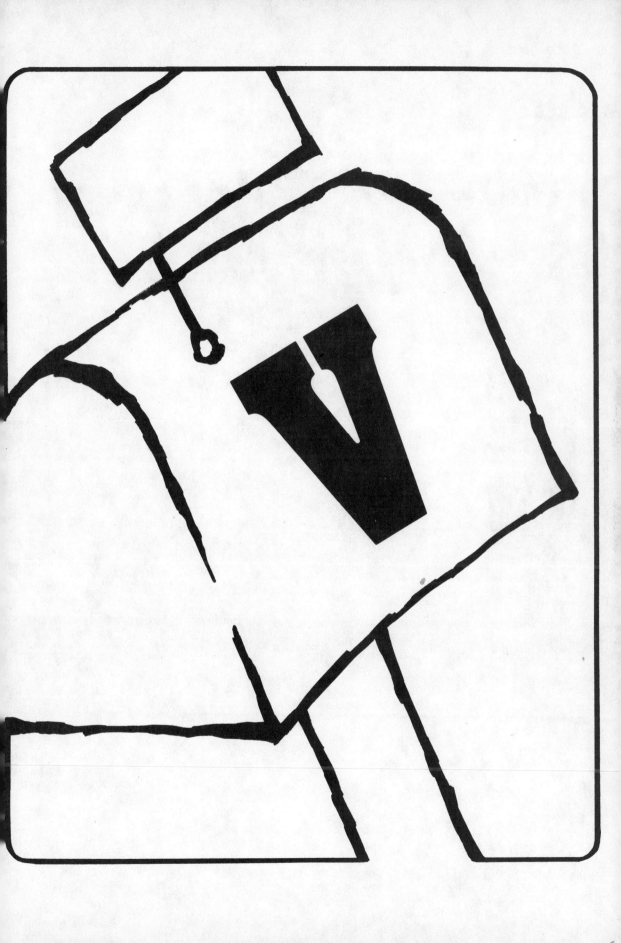

Vacation Exchange Club
350 Broadway
New York, NY 10013
arrangements for exchanging homes/apartments for vacations; Mary DeBaldo, president

Vaccaro, Brenda
c/o Wm. Morris
151 El Camino Drive
Beverly Hills, CA 90212
actress

Vader, Darth
c/o Lucasfilms
P.O. Box 8669
Universal City, CA 91608
villain

Valenti, Jack
1600 I St. NW
Washington DC 20006
president, Motion Picture Association

Valentine, Karen
c/o ICPR
9255 Sunset Blvd.
Los Angeles, CA 90069
actress

Valentino
24 Via Gregoriana
Rome, Italy
fashion designer

Valentino, Thomas
151 W. 46th St.
New York, NY 10036
sound effects recording expert

Vallee, Rudy
c/o Meiklejohn Associates
9250 Wilshire Blvd.
Beverly Hills, CA 90212
crooner

Valli, Frankie
c/o Private Stock Records
40 W. 57th St.
New York, NY 10023
singer

Vampire Research Center Of America
76-03 45th Ave.
Elmhurst, NY 11373
Dr. Stephen Kaplan, researcher

Van Buren, Abigail
c/o Contemporary-Korman Artists
132 Lasky Drive
Beverly Hills, CA 90212
syndicated columnist (Dear Abby)

Vance, Cyrus
U.S. State Department
Washington DC 20520
secretary of state

Vanderbilt, Gloria
498 7th Ave.
New York, NY 10018
designer

Vanderbilt, Oliver
1700 Market St.
Philadelphia, PA 19103
financier

Van Dong, Pham
Office of the President
Hanoi, Vietnam
president of Vietnam

Van Dyke, Dick
P.O. Box 666
Cave Creek, AZ 85331
actor

Vannelli, Gino
c/o BNB Associates
9495 Wilshire Blvd.
Beverly Hills, CA 90212
singer

Vanocur, Sander
c/o ABC News
1124 Connecticut Ave. NW
Washington DC 20036
journalist

Van Patten, Dick
c/o MEW Company
151 San Vicente Blvd.
Beverly Hills, CA 90211
actor

Vaughan, Sarah
c/o Wm. Morris
151 El Camino Drive
Beverly Hills, CA 90212
singer

Vaughn, Robert
9530 Heather Road
Beverly Hills, CA 90210
actor

Veech, Bill
c/o Comishey Park
Dan Ryan at 35th St.
Chicago, IL 60616
owner, Chicago White Sox

Vereen, Ben
c/o Wm. Morris
151 El Camino Dr.
Beverly Hills, CA 90212
actor, entertainer

Vesco, Robert L.
Guana Castle Farm
Costa Rica
fugitive businessman

Vidal, Gore
21 Via di Torre Argentina
Rome, Italy
author

Vigoda, Abe
c/o Contemporary-Korman
Artists
132 Lasky Drive
Beverly Hills, CA 90212
actor

Vilas, Guillermo
c/o Guy, Cromwell, Betz
Pembroke One Building
Suite 525
Virginia Beach, VA 23462
tennis player

Village People
c/o Casablanca Records
8255 Sunset Blvd.
Los Angeles, CA 90046
music group

Villechaize, Herve
c/o ABC TV
4151 Prospect Ave.
Los Angeles, CA 90027
actor

Vincent, Allen
P.O. Box 1981
San Francisco, CA 94101
leader, American Nazi Party

Vincent, Jan-Michael
c/o ICPR
9255 Sunset Blvd.
Los Angeles, CA 90069
actor

Vinton, Bobby
P.O. Box 767
Pacific Palisades, CA 90272
entertainer

Visa
P.O. Box 8999
San Francisco, CA 94128
D.W. Hock, president

Voight, Jon
c/o TRAC Productions
10201 W. Pico Blvd.
Los Angeles, CA 90067
actor

Volker, Paul
Office of Saver &
Consumer Affairs
Washington DC 20551
federal reserve system director

**Volkswagen
of America**
818 Sylvan Ave.
Englewood Cliffs, NJ 07632
Toni Schmuecher, president

**von Furstenberg,
Diane**
530 7th Ave.
New York, NY 10018
designer

Vonnegut, Kurt Jr.
Scudder's Lane
W. Barnstable, MA 02668
author

von Sydow, Max
c/o Kohner-Levy
9169 Sunset Blvd.
Los Angeles, CA 90069
actor

Vreeland, Diana
550 Park Ave.
New York, NY 10021
fashion journalist

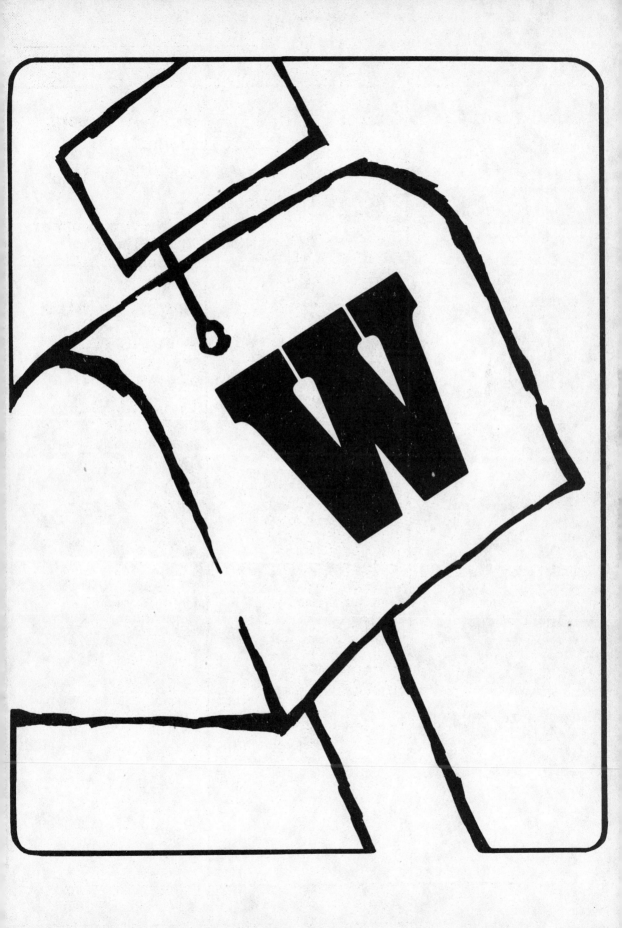

Wade, Virginia
c/o International
Management Group
1 Erieview Plaza
Cleveland, OH 44114
tennis player

Waggoner, Joe D. Jr.
House Office Building
Washington DC 20515
U.S. representative

Waggoner, Lyle
c/o Gibson Agency
9000 Sunset Blvd.
Los Angeles, CA 90069
actor

Wagner, Lindsay
c/o Ron Samuels Management
280 S. Beverly Drive
Beverly Hills, CA 90210
actress

Wagner, Robert
c/o Rogers & Cowan
9665 Wilshire Blvd.
Beverly Hills, CA 90212
actor

Wagner, Robert F.
425 Park Ave.
New York, NY 10022
*attorney, former
mayor of New York*

Wagner, Sherle
Sherle Wagner
International Inc.
60 E. 57th St.
New York, NY 10022
luxury bathroom outfitter

Wainwright, James
1402 N. Havenhurst Drive
Los Angeles, CA 90048
actor

Waite, Ralph
c/o Creative Artists Agency
1888 Century Park E.
Suite 1400
Los Angeles, CA 90067
actor

Wakeman, Rick
c/o Beldock
565 5th Ave.
New York, NY 10017
composer, musician

Wald, Jeff
9356 Santa Monica Blvd.
Beverly Hills, CA 90210
talent manager

Waldheim, Kurt
United Nations
New York, NY 10017
U.N. secretary-general

Walinsky, Adam
1345 Avenue of the Americas
New York, NY 10019
CIA critic; attorney

Walker, Jimmy
c/o The Artists Agency
190 N. Canon Drive
Beverly Hills, CA 90210
actor, comedian

Walker, Nancy
P.O. Box 4475
North Hollywood, CA 91607
actress

Wallace, Cornelia
c/o Ira De Ment
555 S. Perry
Montgomery, AL 36104
*former wife of
George Wallace*

Wallace, Dewitt
Byram Lake Road
Mount Kisco, NY 10549
publisher, Reader's Digest

Wallace, George
3465 Norman Bride Road
Montgomery, AL 36105
former governor

Wallace, Irving
P.O. Box 49328
Los Angeles, CA 90049
author

Wallace, Mike
c/o CBS News
524 W. 57th St.
New York, NY 10019
journalist

Wallach, Eli
90 Riverside Drive
New York, NY 10024
actor

Wallechinsky, David
c/o Wm. Morrow Co.
105 Madison Ave.
New York, NY 10016
author

Wallich, Henry C.
Federal Reserve Board
Washington DC 20551
economist

Wallop, Malcom
Senate Office Building
Washington DC 20510
senator from Wyoming

Walston, Ray
c/o Mickey Freeman
8732 Sunset Blvd.
Los Angeles, CA 90069
actor

Walter, Jessica
c/o Creative Artists Agency
1888 Century Park E.
Suite 1400
Los Angeles, CA 90067
actress

Walters, Barbara
c/o ABC TV
1330 Avenue of the Americas
New York, NY 10019
journalist

Walton, Bill
c/o San Diego Clippers
3500 Sports Arena Blvd.
San Diego, CA 92110
basketball player

Wambaugh, Joseph
P.O. Box 8262
San Marino, CA 91108
author, former police officer

Ward, Burt
9465 Wilshire Blvd. Suite 608
Beverly Hills, CA 90210
actor

Warden, Jack
c/o APA
9000 Sunset Blvd. Suite 315
Los Angeles, CA 90069
actor

Warfield, Paul
c/o Cleveland Browns
Cleveland Stadium
Cleveland, OH 44114
football player

Warhol, Andy
860 Broadway
New York, NY 10003
artist

Warner Brothers Films
4000 Warner Blvd.
Burbank, CA 91505
Frank Wells, president

Warner Communications Co.
10 Rockefeller Plaza
New York, NY 10020
Steven Ross, president

Warner, Jack Jr.
107 N. Gunston
Los Angeles, CA 90049
producer, writer

Warner, John W.
Atoka Farm
P.O. Box 1320
Middleburg, VA 22117
senator from Virginia; former secretary of the navy

Warnke, Paul C.
U.S. Arms Control & Disarmament Agency
Washington DC 20510
agency director

Warren, Charles
722 Jackson Place NW
Washington DC 20006
chairman of Council on Environmental Quality

Warren, Gerald L.
San Diego Union
P.O. Box 191
San Diego, CA 92112
editor, former deputy press secretary to Nixon

Warwick, Dionne
c/o Paul Cantor Enterprises
144 S. Beverly Drive
Beverly Hills, CA 90212
singer

Washington, Walter E.
District Building
Washington DC 20004
mayor of Washington DC

Wasserman, Lew
c/o MCA
Universal Studios
Universal City, CA 91608
MCA president

Waters, Muddy
c/o Cameron
320 S. Warola Ave.
La Grange, IL 60525
singer

Watson, Charles "Tex"
California Men's Colony
San Luis Obispo, CA 93401
convicted mass murderer, member of Manson family

Watson, Doc
Route 1
P.O. Box 34
Deep Gup, NC 28618
singer

Watson, Tom
726 Commerce Tower
Kansas City, MO 64105
golfer

Weaver, Dennis
c/o Universal Studios
100 Universal City Plaza
Universal City, CA 91608
actor

Weaver, Fritz
c/o Kroll Agency
390 West End Ave.
New York, NY 10023
actor

Webb, Jack
P.O. Box 69336
Los Angeles, CA 90069
actor, producer

Webb, Jimmy
c/o Katz-Gallin-Morey
9255 Sunset Blvd.
Los Angeles, CA 90069
composer

Webb, Spider
12 W. 1st Ave.
Mt. Vernon, NY 10550
tattoo artist

Weicker, Lowell P. Jr.
Senate Office Building
Washington DC 20510
senator from Connecticut

Weight Watchers Inc.
800 Community Drive
Manhasset, NY 11030
Albert Lippert, president

Wein, George
311 W. 74th St.
New York, NY 10023
producer of
Newport Jazz Festival

Weinberger,
Casper W.
Becktel Corporation
50 Beale St.
San Francisco, CA 94105
former secretary of HEW

Weintraub, Jerry
9744 Wilshire Blvd.
Beverly Hills, CA 90212
talent producer and manager

Weiss, Cora
c/o Friends Shipment
777 United Nations Plaza
Rm. 10G
New York, NY 10017
peace activist

Weiss, Nat
888 7th Ave.
New York, NY 10019
theatrical lawyer

Weiss, Theodore
26 Haslet St.
Princeton, NJ 08540
poet, editor

Weissmuller, Johnny
Motion Picture Country Home
23450 Calabasas
Woodland Hills, CA 91364
former "Tarzan"

Welch, Raquel
c/o Wm. Morris
151 El Camino Drive
Beverly Hills, CA 90212
actress

Welch, Robert
395 Concord Ave.
Belmont, MA 02178
president, John Birch Society

Weld, Tuesday
c/o ICM
8899 Beverly Blvd.
Los Angeles, CA 90048
actress

Weldon, Steve
c/o Spaghetti Eating Contest
Austin Chamber of Commerce
Austin, TX 78700
champion spaghetti eater – ate
a pound of spaghetti
in 48 seconds

Welk, Lawrence
100 Wilshire Blvd.
Santa Monica, CA 90401
orchestra leader

Welles, Orson
c/o Weissberger
120 E. 56th St.
New York, NY 10022
producer, actor

Wells, Kitty
264 Old Hickory Road
Madison, TN 37115
singer

Wendelstedt, Harry
88 S St.
Andres Drive
Ormond Beach, FL 32074
*named top umpire
in baseball*

**Wendy's
Hamburgers**
4288 W. Dublin
Dublin, OH 43017
R. David Thomas, president

Wenner, Jann
745 5th Ave.
New York, NY 10022
*founder and publisher,
Rolling Stone*

Wesolowski, Paul G.
1017 Belfield Ave.
Drexel Hill, PA 19026
authority on Marx Brothers

West, Dottie
P.O. Box 12514
Nashville, TN 37212
singer

West, Jerry
c/o Los Angeles Lakers
3900 W. Manchester Blvd.
Los Angeles, CA 90306
basketball coach

West, Mae
570 N. Rossmore Ave.
Los Angeles, CA 90004
actress

Western Union
1 Lake St.
Upper Saddle River,
NJ 07458
Russell McFall, president

**Westinghouse
Electric Company**
Gateway Center
Westinghouse Blvd.
Pittsburgh, PA 15222
Robert Kirby, president

**Westmoreland, Gen.
William Childs**
107½ Tradd St.
Charleston, SC 29401
U.S. Army general

Westwood, Jean
5302 N. 79th Place
Scottsdale, AZ 85253
*former chairperson,
Republican National
Committee*

**Whirlpool
Corporation**
Lake Shore & Monte Road
Benton Harbor, MI 49022
John Platts, president

Whitaker, Dr. J.
University of Tennessee
800 Madison Ave.
Memphis, TN 38163
*neurologist specializing in
multiple sclerosis*

Whitaker, John
P.O. Box 342
Bridgehampton, NY 19932
sportscaster

White, Betty
c/o Wm. Morris
151 El Camino Drive
Beverly Hills, CA 90212
actress

White, Byron
U.S. Supreme Court
Washington DC 20543
justice

White, Dan
California Medical Facility
Vacaville, CA 95688
convicted murderer

White, Kevin
Office of the Mayor
City Hall
Boston, MA 02201
mayor of Boston

White, Theodore
168 E. 64th St.
New York, NY 10021
author

Whitmore, James
c/o The Blake Agency
409 N. Camden Drive
Beverly Hills, CA 90210
actor

Whitney, Margaret A.
MAW's Secretarial Service
3660 Wilshire Blvd. #344
Los Angeles, CA 90010
*speed typist (155 words
per minute)*

The Who
c/o Sir Productions
130 W. 57th St.
New York, NY 10019
music group

Widmark, Richard
999 Potrero Road
Thousand Oaks, CA 91360
actor

Wiggins, Charles E.
House Office Building
Washington DC 20515
U.S. representative

Wigle, Ernest
101 College St.
Toronto, Ontario M5G 1L7
Canada
cardiologist

Wilbur, Dr. Cornelia
408 Bristol Road
Lexington, KY 40502
*psychiatrist specializing in
schizophrenia and
multiple personalities*

Wilcoxen, John
5748 Auburn Blvd.
Sacramento, CA 95841
*stand-in for George Reeves
in "Superman"
television series*

Wilde, Cornel
c/o Morgan Company
6300 Wilshire Blvd.
Los Angeles, CA 90048
actor, producer, director

Wilder, Billy
c/o Universal Studios
Universal City, CA 91608
director

Wilder, Brooks
3000 Sand Hill Road
Menlo Park, CA 94025
pollution control expert

Wilder, Gene
c/o Kaplan & Veidt
667 Madison Ave.
New York, NY 10021
director, actor, writer

Wildmon, Donald E.
1208 Zentwood
Tupelo, MS 38801
*president, National
Federation for Decency
on Television*

Wileh, Richard E.
3818 N. Woodrow St.
Arlington, VA 22207
*former chairman, Federal
Communications
Commission*

Wiley, William
605 3rd Ave.
New York, NY 10016
publisher

Wilkins, Roy
147-15 Village Road
Jamaica, NY 11435
civil rights leader

Will, George
1150 15th St. NW
Washington, DC 20005
editor, political columnist

Wille, Frank
4733 Berkeley Terrace
Washington DC 20007
*former chairman,
Federal Deposit
Insurance Corporation*

Willet, Henry
10 E. Moreland Ave.
Philadelphia, PA 19118
stained glass artist

Williams, Andy
816 N. La Cienega Blvd.
Los Angeles, CA 90069
singer

Williams, Anson
c/o ABC TV
4151 Prospect Ave.
Los Angeles, CA 90027
actor, singer

Williams, Barry
c/o ICM
8899 Beverly Blvd.
Los Angeles, CA 90048
actor

Williams, Betty
Peace House
224 Lisburn Road
Belfast 9, Northern Ireland
peace activist

Williams, Billy Dee
c/o ICM
40 W. 57th St.
New York, NY 10019
actor

Williams, Cindy
c/o Paramount TV
5451 Marathon St.
Hollywood, CA 90038
actress

Williams, Edward Bennett
Democratic National
Committee
Hill Building
Washington DC 20006
attorney

Williams, Esther
9377 Readcrest
Beverly Hills, CA 90210
swimmer, actress

Williams, Harrison A. Jr.
Senate Office Building
Washington DC 20510
senator from New Jersey

Williams, Rev. Hosea L.
Southern Christian
Leadership Conference
334 Auburn Ave. NE
Atlanta, GA 30303
civil rights leader

Williams, John
P.O. Box 900
Beverly Hills, CA 90213
composer

Williams, Paul
c/o Entertainment Artists
9200 Sunset Blvd.
Los Angeles, CA 90269
composer, singer, actor

Williams, Robin
c/o Estelle Endler
3920 Sunny Oak Road
Sherman Oaks, CA 91403
comedian, actor

Williams, Ted
P.O. Box 481
Islam Orada, FL 33036
*member of baseball
Hall of Fame*

Williams, Tennessee
c/o ICM
40 W. 57th St.
New York, NY 10019
playwright

Willig, George
88 E. 193rd St.
New York, NY 10037
*"human fly" who climbed
the World Trade Center*

Wills, Frank
c/o Dorothy Evans
1025 Connecticut Ave. NW
#506
Washington DC 20006
*security guard who caught
Watergate burglars*

Wilson, Dr. C.B.
University of California
San Francisco, CA 94143
*surgeon specializing
in brain tumors*

Wilson, Dorothy
114 Forest Ave.
Orono, ME 04473
author

Wilson, Earl
340 W. 57th St.
New York, NY 10019
columnist, commentator

Wilson, Flip
c/o Thirteen Productions
2049 Century Park E.
Suite 3340
Los Angeles, CA 90067
comedian

Wilson, Malcolm
Bar Building
White Plains, NY 12601
former governor

Wilson, Nancy
c/o Levy Enterprises
8570 Sunset Blvd.
Los Angeles, CA 90069
singer

Wilson Sporting Goods
2233 West St.
River Grove, IL 60171
F.L. Peck, president

Winchell, Paul
14136 Janna Way
Sylmar, CA 91342
ventriloquist

Windsor, Duchess of
4 rue du Champ d'
Entrainment
Paris, 75016 France
*widow of late Duke of
Windsor, formerly King
of England*

Winfield, Paul
6300 Wilshire Blvd.
Los Angeles, CA 90048
actor

Winkler, Henry
P.O. Box 1764
Studio City, CA 91604
actor

Winkler, Irwin
c/o MGM Studios
10202 Washington Blvd.
Culver City, CA 90230
producer

Winston Tire Co.
2101 W. Alameda
Burbank, CA 91506
Sam Winston, president

**Winter, Edgar
& Johnny**
c/o Blue Sky Records
745 5th Ave.
New York, NY 10022
rock and blues musicians

Winter, Paul
P.O. Box 68
Litchfield, CT 06759
musican

Winter, William
Office of the Governor
Jackson, MS 39205
governor of Mississippi

Winters, Jonathan
Arcola Ave.
Toluca Lake, CA 91602
comedian, actor

Winters, Shelley
c/o ICM
8899 Beverly Blvd.
Los Angeles, CA 90048
actress

Wise, Robert
c/o MGM Studios
10202 Washington Blvd.
Culver City, CA 90230
producer, director

Wolfe, Tom
c/o Farrar, Straus &
Giroux Inc.
19 Union Square West
New York, NY 10003
author

Wolper, David
c/o Warner Brothers
4000 Warner Blvd.
Burbank, CA 91522
producer

**Women's
International Zionist
Organization**
P.O. Box 33159
38 David Hamelech Blvd.
Tel-Aviv, Israel
*Mrs. Raya Jaglom,
president*

Wonder, Stevie
c/o Jonz
6255 Sunset Blvd. 17th Floor
Los Angeles, CA 90028
singer, songwriter

Wood, Natalie
c/o Rogers & Cowan
9665 Wilshire Blvd.
Beverly Hills, CA 90212
actress

Wood, Wilbur
c/o Chicago White Sox
Chicago White Sox Park
Chicago, IL 60616
baseball player

Woods, Dr. J.E.
Mayo Graduate School
of Medicine
Rochester, MN 55901
*plastic surgeon specializing
in neck and breast
reconstruction*

Woods, Rose Mary
716 Jackson Place NW
Washington DC 20006
*former personal secretary
to Richard Nixon*

Woodcock, Leonard
U.S. State Department
Washington DC 20500
*U.S. ambassador to
China; former labor leader*

Wooden, John
405 Hilgard Ave.
Los Angeles, CA 90024
*former UCLA
basketball coach*

**Woodiwiss,
Kathleen W.**
c/o Avon Books
959 8th Ave.
New York, NY 10019
author

Woodward, Bob
1150 15th St. NW
Washington DC 20005
*reporter who uncovered
Watergate scandal; author*

Woodward, Joanne
Coleytown Road
Westport, CT 00880
actress, director

Woolley, Catherine
Higgins Hollow Road
Truro, MA 02666
author

F.W. Woolworth Co.
233 Broadway
New York, NY 10007
E.F. Gibbons, president

Worden, Al
250 Royal Palm Way
Palm Beach, FL 33480
astronaut

World Pen Pals Club
1690 Como Ave.
St. Paul, MN 55108
Lonija Fazenden, secretary

Worth, Irene
c/o ICM
40 W. 57th St.
New York, NY 10019
actress

Wouk, Herman
c/o Little Brown Company
34 Beacon St.
Boston, MA 02114
author

Wrangler Jeans
335 Church Court
Greensboro, NC 27401
E.A. Morris, president

Wray, Fay
2160 Century Park E.
Los Angeles, CA 90067
actress

Wright, John & Carol
664 N. Michigan Ave.
Chicago, IL 60611
*co-presidents, Vitamin
Information Organization*

Wright, James C. Jr.
House Office Building
Washington DC 20515
U.S. representative

Wright, Lloyd
858 N. Doheny Drive
Los Angeles, CA 90069
*architect; son of Frank
Lloyd Wright*

Wrigley, William
410 N. Michigan Ave.
Chicago, IL 60611
corporate executive

Wyatt, Jane
c/o Wm. Morris
151 El Camino Drive
Beverly Hills, CA 90212
actress

Wyler, William
1121 Summit Drive
Beverly Hills, CA 90210
producer, director

Wyeth, Andrew
Chadds Ford, PA 19317
artist

Wyman, Jane
1567 W. Holman Ave.
Los Angeles, CA 90024
actress

Wynette, Tammy
c/o Lavender-Blake Agency
1217 16th Ave. S.
Nashville, TN 37212
singer

Wynn, Early
P.O. Box 218
Nohomus, FL 33555
*member of baseball
Hall of Fame*

Wynn, Keenan
c/o Robinson & Associates
132 S. Rodeo Drive
Beverly Hills, CA 90212
actor

Xenakis, Iannis
17 rue Victor Masee
Paris 75009
France
composer, architect

Xerox Corporation
Stamford, CT 06904
C. Peter McColough,
president

YWCA
600 Lexington Ave.
New York, NY 10022
*Sara-Alyce P. Wright,
executive director*

Yablans, Frank
781 5th Ave.
New York, NY 10023
producer

Yablonski, Joseph A. Jr.
1150 Connecticut Ave. NW
Washington, DC 20036
attorney

Yarborough, William "Cale"
c/o Stock Car
Racing Association
1801 Volusia Ave.
Daytona Beach, FL 32015
stock car racer

Yarrow, Peter
P.O. Box 135
Bearsville, NY 12409
folk singer

Yastrzemski,, Carl
24 Jersey St.
Boston, MA 02215
baseball player

Yates, Peter
c/o ICM
40 W. 57th St.
New York, NY 10019
director

Yepremian, Garo
814 N. Federal Highway
Hallandale, FL 33009
football player

Yo, Ming Lun
Building 480
Brookhaven National
Laboratory
Upton, NY 11973
*developed system of burning
waste heat directly into
electrical energy*

York, Michael
c/o ICM
8899 Beverly Blvd.
Los Angeles, CA 90048
actor

York, Susannah
c/o ICM
8899 Beverly Blvd.
Los Angeles, CA 90048
actress

Yorkin, Bud
1901 Avenue of the Stars
Los Angeles, CA 90067
producer, director

Yorty, Samuel
3435 Wilshire Blvd.
Los Angeles, CA 90010
former mayor of Los Angeles

Young, Andrew
101 Marietta Tower
Blvd. NW
Atlanta, GA 30303
former U.N. ambassador

Young, Coleman A.
Office of the Mayor
City Hall
2 Woodward Ave.
Detroit, MI 48226
mayor of Detroit

Young, Dr. Jerome
3051 Chapel Ave.
Cherry Hill, NJ 08002
*first man to undergo
three heart transplants*

Young, John
Manned Spacecraft Center
NASA
Houston, TX 77058
astronaut

Young, Loretta
c/o Wm. Morris
151 El Camino Drive
Beverly Hills, CA 90212
actress

Young, Milton R.
Senate Office Building
Washington DC 20510
senator from North Dakota

Young, Neil
c/o Lookout Management
9120 Sunset Blvd.
Los Angeles, CA 90069
singer, songwriter

Young, Robert
c/o Herb Tannen
6640 Sunset Blvd.
Hollywood, CA 90028
actor

**Young Ochowicz,
Sheila**
12500 Wade St.
Detroit, MI 48213
speed skater

Younger, Evelle J.
3580 Wilshire Blvd.
Los Angeles, CA 90010
*former California attorney
general*

Youngman, Henny
77 W. 55th St.
New York, NY 10019
comedian

Zappa, Frank
c/o Glotzer Management
824 N. Robertson Blvd.
Los Angeles, CA 90069
singer, songwriter

Zawacki, Dr. B.
University of
Southern California
L.A. County Medical Center
Los Angeles, CA 90033
*pediatric and adult
burn specialist*

Zenith Company
1000 N. Milwaukee Ave.
Glenview, IL 60025
John Nevin, president

Ziegler, Ronald L.
c/o Syska & Hennessy
1720 I St. NW
Washington DC 20006
former Nixon press secretary

Zimbalist, Efrem Sr.
2255 Lindley Way
Reno, NV 89502
violinist

Zimbalist, Efrem Jr.
c/o Guttman & Pam
120 El Camino Drive
Beverly Hills, CA 90212
actor

Zimbalist, Stephanie
c/o ICM
8899 Beverly Blvd.
Los Angeles, CA 99048
actress

Zimmer, Don
24 Yawkey Way
Boston, MA 02215
*publisher, Baseball
Club Magazine*

Zindel, Paul
c/o Brown Ltd.
60 E. 56th St.
New York, NY 10022
playwright

Zorina, Vera
c/o Barrett
1860 Broadway
New York, NY 10023
dancer, actress

Zorinsky, Edward
Senate Office Building
Washington DC 20510
senator from Nebraska

Zucher, Mitchell
P.O. Box 1023
Mendocino, CA 95460
*inventor of a solar/wind
water pump*

Zumwalt, Elmo R. Jr.
c/o American
Medical Buildings
515 W.Wells St.
Milwaukee, WI 53203
retired admiral

ARE YOU ANYONE?

We plan to update HOW TO REACH ANYONE WHO'S ANYONE periodically, and you can play an active role in that endeavor. If you are notable in any field, or know someone who is, send the name, mailing address and some documentation of the notability for possible inclusion in our next edition.

Thank you,

Michael Levine
PRICE/STERN/SLOAN PUBLISHERS, Inc.
410 N. La Cienega Blvd.
Los Angeles, CA 90048

pss!®